Young Readers Edition

ANIMAL BEHAVIOR

Niko Tinbergen

and the Editors of TIME-LIFE BOOKS

TIME-LIFE BOOKS, NEW YORK

ON THE COVER: A female swan
broods her young in a nest. Such
behavior is common among birds; but
swan chicks are unusual in one way.
Though they can swim and feed
themselves right after hatching, they
often remain with their parents for as
long as nine months.

Contents

1 Animal Behavior: an Infant Science   7

2 The Sense Organs and How They Work   19

3 The Signs That Animals Respond To   35

4 The Machinery That Makes Things Go   55

5 How Animals Find Their Way About   75

6 Is Behavior Born or Learned in Animals?   93

7 Living Together in Order to Survive   109

Index   126
For Further Reading   128
Credits and Acknowledgments   128

Introduction

The study of animal behavior began with early man's first attempts to understand the creatures around him. Today it is still one of the most complex and challenging branches of all science. In fact, at present we seem closer to understanding the origins of life itself than we are to understanding how and why most living things behave as they do.

This understanding does not depend on advanced mathematics, on delicate instruments or on giant computers. An experienced student of animal behavior, armed with binoculars and hidden in a blind, can gather in a few hours enough facts about his subject to keep him thinking for a year. Some behaviorists experiment with animals in the laboratory; others prefer to watch them undisturbed in their surroundings because they believe that the animal's behavior has helped the species to survive and evolve under the conditions of the environment.

Behavior study is not a field for narrow specialists. The author, Dr. Tinbergen, has had wide experience and he adds deep insights here to create a fascinating volume, which constitutes not only a challenge but an encouragement to every reader. Anyone, Dr. Tinbergen seems to say, who has a sharp eye and ear, is patient and does not jump to conclusions can learn a great deal by studying animals, and he might even make observations of lasting value to science.

KENNETH D. ROEDER
Professor of Physiology
Department of Biology
Tufts University

1

Animal Behavior:
an Infant Science

The vast majority of people, wherever they live and whatever they do, come in contact with animals in one way or another and have to deal with them. The hunter has to know the ways of his quarry. The farmer must be aware of the habits of his animals and of creatures that damage his crops. The fisherman must know when and where to find his fish and how to outwit them. Even the modern city dweller meets animals. He may want to get rid of the cockroaches in his kitchen, or he may keep a dog or bird as a pet and grow familiar with the way it behaves. All over the world, among primitive tribes as well as in modern society, there are those who delight in the observation of animals.

As a science, however, the study of animal behavior is still quite new. It is concerned with far more than just recording interest-

AMONG THE DUNES of Ravenglass in northern England, Niko Tinbergen, author of this book, strolls with binoculars in hand while his pet crow trails behind. Tinbergen spends much of his time in the field, watching how animals behave in nature. From these observations he draws ideas for his theories.

ing incidents of animal life. It tries to find out exactly why animals behave the way they do—what "makes them tick."

Where do we begin? What exactly *is* animal behavior? Roughly speaking, it includes all the movements animals make. These involve walking, running, swimming and crawling, as well as the movements animals make when feeding, when mating, even when breathing. Nor is this all. Slight movements of parts of the body, such as pricking up the ears or making a sound, are also parts of behavior. Many animals do something similar to our blushing: they change color, sometimes as a way of hiding from enemies, sometimes to frighten away other creatures, sometimes to attract a female during courting. Behavior can also consist of just standing still and looking intently, or "thinking"—things that may influence the way an animal behaves next.

Animals behave in many ways—as many ways, in fact, as their different shapes, sizes and colors. No two species act exactly alike. A robin can be recognized by its own special song, by the way it pecks and hops around on one's lawn, by the kind of nest it builds and by the way it reacts to enemies and to its own mates. Of course, one species of animal may do the same thing in several different ways. Gulls may feed by diving for fish in the sea, but they also may kill a sick bird, or paddle their feet to drive worms to the surface of a meadow, or even grab insects on the wing.

Why does an animal behave the way it does? This seems like a simple question. But it is really two questions in one.

Let us say we are watching a dog eat. When we ask ourselves, "Why is it eating?" we may mean, "What is the *use* of eating?" In this case, of course, the answer is that it eats in order to survive. But if we mean, "What *makes* it eat?" we are not inquiring about the effects of its behavior but about its causes. Now it becomes useful to know whether or not the dog has been starved, whether it is stimulated by the sight and smell of food and whether it learned where and when to seek food when it was young.

Right now the study of the survival value of behavior is in a very interesting phase. About one hundred years ago Charles Darwin shook the world with his theory of evolution through "natural selection." Darwin said that the wonderful adaptedness of the plants and animals we see around us was not due to sudden creation but to a long process of evolution. Through the ages, he said, only those plants and animals survived that had characteristics or abilities that could be adapted to a changing environment. Organisms had become what they were through the continuous selection of the fittest individuals, who outbred the less well-adapted ones.

This theory soon led people to investigate all sorts of animal peculiarities to see if they really contributed to fitness. Many fascinating discoveries were made about so-called "adaptive behavior." One of the most famous cases is that of the yucca moth and the yucca flower.

The female yucca moth is one of the few moths equipped with a special tube called an ovipositor through which it lays its eggs. This tiny tube is needle-sharp so that the moth can thrust it into the yucca flower to lay the eggs inside. While doing this, it collects the pollen inside the yucca and fertilizes the flower. This act of fertilization means that the flower will bear seeds. This, in turn, means that the larvae of the moth, which live on the seeds, will have a plentiful supply of food as they develop in the flow-er. Since there are many more seeds than the moth larvae can possibly eat, the plant is not harmed. This form of cooperation guarantees the survival of both the moth and the plant.

Another example of adaptive behavior is the small fish called the stickleback, which builds a nest like a little open tube in the water. After persuading one or more females to lay eggs in the nest, the male stickleback guards the nest in an interesting way: it alternately swims around the nest and "fans" it, directing water at it by moving its fins in quick, regular strokes.

Why does the stickleback do this? A few

Three Pioneers in Animal Behavior

CHARLES DARWIN (1809-1882) was the first scientist to recognize that the way an animal behaved helped it to survive. Before him, most scientists had judged animal behavior by human standards, or ignored it.

J. HENRI FABRE (1823-1915) was the first to make detailed observations of animals in the wild. He spent 40 years watching bees and wasps in his garden in France, and proved how complex their behavior was.

IVAN PAVLOV (1849-1936) developed the theory of the "conditioned reflex." In his tests, he rang a bell every time his dogs were about to be fed. Soon, the dogs' mouths would water as a reflex whenever the bell rang.

Watching Bees and Ants

The two animal behavior experts shown here are famous for their work with insects. Theodore C. Schneirla *(far right)* studies the learning ability of ants by sending them through a test maze in his laboratory at New York's American Museum of Natural History. He has discovered that ants are among the best learners of all insects: they can memorize the correct paths to food in one maze and can apply this learning to other mazes. Karl von Frisch *(right)* tests the color vision of bees in the garden of his Austrian home, using yellow cards to attract them. Fifty years ago von Frisch proved by similar color-card experiments that bees are not color-blind, as scientists had thought, but are attracted to brightly colored flowers, which they pollinate.

simple experiments have provided the simple answer. It is "ventilating" the eggs, keeping them supplied with freshly aerated water, which pushes aside the stale water around the eggs and gives them the oxygen they need. If the male is removed, the eggs die. They also die if the male is allowed to stay and fan but is separated from them by a piece of glass. They do not die if the male is removed and replaced by a glass tube through which water is regularly directed at the nest. But it must be freshly aerated water and it must be aimed at the nest; if the tube stops delivering water or if stale water is pumped through it, the eggs will not survive.

Another fascinating example of adaptive behavior for survival is that of the black-headed gulls. These birds, which nest in large groups in sand dunes by the sea, like many other birds take away the empty egg shell each time a chick has hatched. Why do they do this? We thought it likely that this was useful in protecting their young from enemies. A piece of shell with its white inside lying right next to the chick might serve as a signal to other animals that there was a meal nearby.

We decided to test this idea. We began our tests with crows, since these birds are the chief enemies of young black-headed gulls. We discovered that nests that had pieces of shell lying within eight inches of them were attacked by crows far more often than those that had no shells. With this important piece of knowledge, our idea began to have some substance. We went on to investigate what other defenses the gulls had against enemies. This led to some fascinating discoveries. For example, we learned that there was a reason for the gulls' habit of all laying their eggs at about the same time: they would all be concerned to defend their eggs at once. This proved to have a direct bearing on survival of the whole brood. Birds laying a little before the others, and birds laying a little after, lost their broods more often to attacks.

The habit of nesting in dense colonies also reduced attacks on the eggs. When we laid out extra eggs in lines running from well inside to well outside the colony, we found that the outside eggs were taken much more often than inside eggs. We also found, through long study, that the gulls' habit of spending nights on broad, open beaches was a very effective defense against

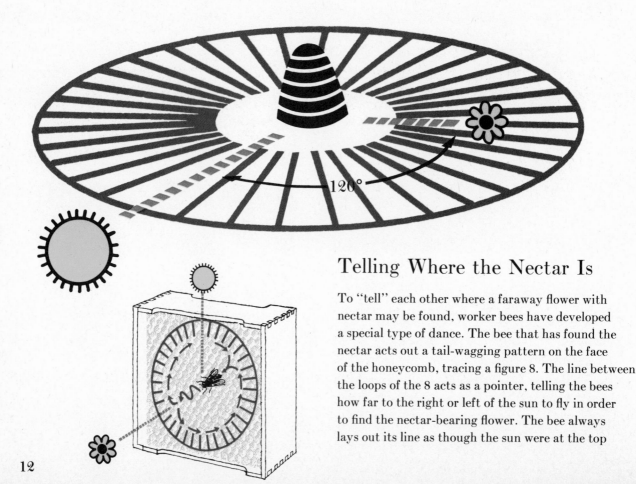

Telling Where the Nectar Is

To "tell" each other where a faraway flower with nectar may be found, worker bees have developed a special type of dance. The bee that has found the nectar acts out a tail-wagging pattern on the face of the honeycomb, tracing a figure 8. The line between the loops of the 8 acts as a pointer, telling the bees how far to the right or left of the sun to fly in order to find the nectar-bearing flower. The bee always lays out its line as though the sun were at the top foxes. Foxes roamed over the beach as well as over the dunes. But they killed many more gulls in the dunes, where the tall grass and humps of sand gave them a better chance to come up on the gulls without being noticed. Only on very dark nights were they able to sneak up and attack the gulls on the beach.

Thus, by observation and experiments, the student gradually becomes aware of how complex and marvelously adapted to living animal behavior is. He begins to see clearly that behavior is indeed an essential part of an animal's equipment for survival.

The movements of an animal in staying alive are often very efficient. The cuttlefish, a relative of the octopus and squid, can get around the defenses of shrimps in a very interesting way. As the cuttlefish swims a few inches above the sandy bottom, it spouts a gentle jet of water at regular intervals, aiming down and a little ahead. Every time it does so, the sand in front is whirled up. The purpose of this becomes clear when one sees the water jet hit a buried shrimp. These shrimps are wonderfully

of the comb. In the drawings at left, the flower lies about 120° to the left of the sun, and the bee shows this angle in its figure 8 on the comb. On this page, the flower is about 70° to the right of the sun and the 8 is laid out to match. In this case the flower is very far away and the bee signals this by wagging its abdomen slowly across the 8. In the first case, the flower is nearer and the bee informs its co-workers by wagging faster.

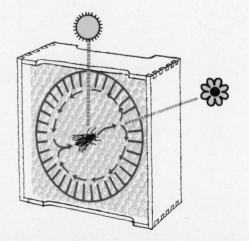

13

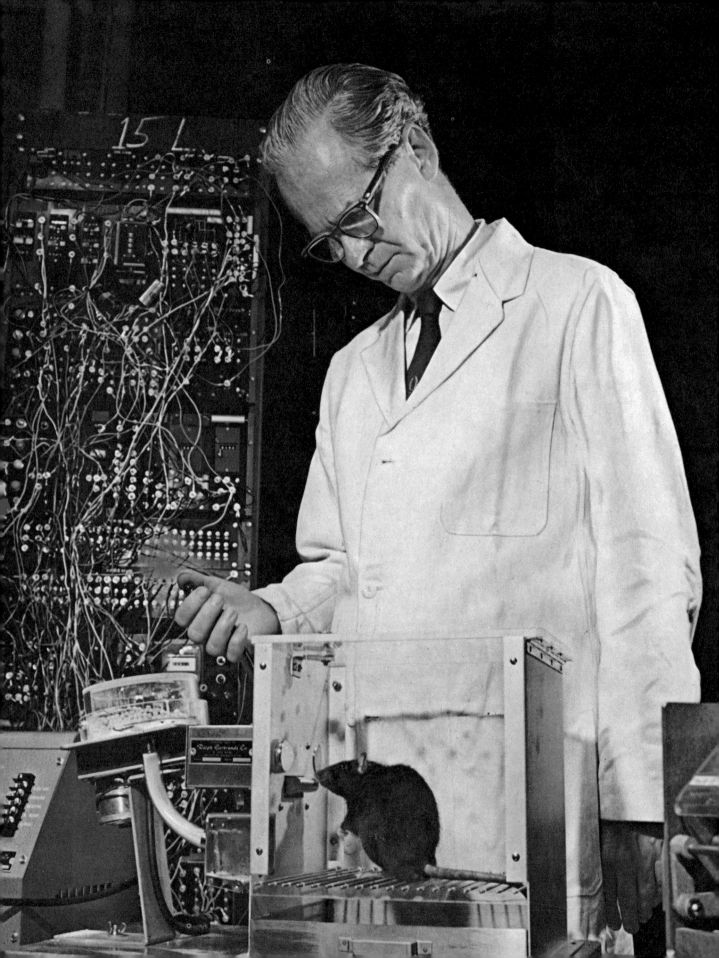

camouflaged to begin with, and they conceal themselves even better by lying under a thin layer of sand, which they sweep over their backs with a wide, backward movement of their two antennae. When a cuttlefish happens to expose a shrimp by whirling away its protective blanket of sand, the shrimp quickly covers itself again. This is its undoing. The cuttlefish, which might have overlooked the shrimp if it had remained still, detects the movement. Instead, the cuttlefish immediately shoots out its tentacles and seizes the shrimp.

In trying to discover why animals behave the way they do, we got involved in some fascinating research of a different kind. We have known for a long time that behavior is a result of muscle activity, and that muscles do not contract unless stimulated by nerves. But rarely is behavior a matter of the contraction of just one muscle. Even simple movements like walking are the result of a whole series of contractions and relaxations of many muscles, all well timed. In fact, behavior is usually a symphony of muscle contractions, guided by messages from the central nervous system.

The central nervous system does not act entirely on its own. It receives stimulation from other sources, including the sense organs: the eyes, ears, nose and others that provide the animal with information about the outside world. But behavior is also controlled from within. When an animal feels hunger, for example, it starts off to find a

A Rat and Its Reward

B. Frederick Skinner of Harvard University experiments in the conditioning of animals by training them to perform unfamiliar acts for food. At far left, Dr. Skinner observes a hungry brown rat in a special mechanical box. In time the rat will learn that to get food it must wait for a light to go on, then press a bar lever that opens a trap door. Above, the rat lunges for the lever as the light flashes, then pokes its head through the door for its reward.

meal; when the sex urge awakes, the animal goes out in search of a mate. Finally, outside stimulation and internal conditions work together. A hungry animal reacts to food while a full animal does not, and outside of the mating season, most animals show little interest in the partners that so strongly attract them during the season.

Confusion arises in the study of animal behavior because many people assume that animals, like humans, can be "angry," or "sad," or "amused." But scientists simply do not know whether or not animals have these human reactions, that an animal attacks because it is "angry" or retreats because it is "afraid." We must also remember that animals cannot think ahead about the results of something they may do, as humans can. Many animals do things—such as building a nest, feeding their young, hoarding food—that prove to be useful long after they do it, but they do not really seem to have these distant aims in mind when they are doing them. Moreover, they often seem unable to handle unusual situations that arise. In such cases their behavior may "misfire." If a young songbird is accidentally kicked out of the nest and gets chilled, it does not open its mouth for food when its parent comes along, so the parent neither feeds it nor cares for it. It dies simply because the parents fail to cope with this unexpected development. The parents take care of only the young that are in the nest and feed only the young that open their mouths. What they react to, much more rigidly than human beings, is the stimulus of the moment.

We are still very far from completely understanding the behavior of animals. But we are beginning to learn how we can arrive at such an understanding. We also feel that our task is urgent. Some animals, such as those we consider pests, are a direct threat to us, to our health and our food supplies. We must know how to keep them in check. Others, such as our cattle and edible fish, are vital to us. They have to be farmed, bred and harvested sensibly. We also have to learn to live and let live, to share our planet with our fellow creatures, and this task of conservation, too, requires understanding. And, finally, since we are related to our fellow animals, a closer study of their behavior can help us understand our own.

Geese Who Love Their "Mother"

Two snow geese nip fondly at the head of the Austrian
behaviorist Konrad Z. Lorenz, who swims with them at his
research institute in Bavaria, Germany. Lorenz'
observations of animals in the wild have taught him how
to talk their own "language" and to impress young ones
into thinking of him as their "mother."

2
The Sense Organs and How They Work

To be efficient, the behavior of animals must include the ability to do the right things at the right times. Unless animals carry out the complicated movements we call behavior at the proper moment and in the proper place, these movements will be useless. In order to do this, however, they must have information about conditions in the outside world. This information reaches them through their sense organs.

Stimulation of the senses is often the starting point of behavior. A dog sees its master put on his hat and immediately barks in anticipation of a walk. Once outside, the dog starts running in pursuit of a scent. Thus he reacts to his environment. Our study of the way behavior is controlled in animals can therefore start with a study of the outside stimulations—or "stimuli"—to which they can respond.

What sort of stimuli do animals receive? They are not always the same stimuli as those to which a human might react, or those to which we might *think* animals would react. Failure to understand this can lead to false conclusions. I once heard of a government official who spent $5,000 on

COMPOUND EYES, common to all insects like the horsefly at left, are made up of thousands of tiny little eyes. Each of these eyes sees a different point on the object the insect looks at. The points create a picture made up of tiny dots—a blurry image compared to the one in the single-lens eye of man.

mothballs to keep birds off the runways of an airport where they collided with jet planes. What he did not know was that birds have a very poorly developed sense of smell—the mothballs might be very effective against other flying creatures like moths, for which they were intended, but they did not bother the birds at all.

Different animals, including man, have different "windows to the world." Some have sensory equipment that is much poorer than ours. In others, the senses are far superior. Some animals even react to stimuli man cannot detect at all: sights, sounds and smells we are unable to sense without artificial extensions to our own sense organs. Bees, for example, see and react to ultraviolet light, while human beings have to use special apparatus to transform the ultraviolet rays into light that we can see.

Once it was realized that animals might have sense organs quite different from our own, scientists began to explore their sensitivity to outside stimuli.

Karl von Frisch, the famous Austrian zoologist, gave this field of research its start. His name is rightly connected with his work on bees. But he and his numerous pupils have also done outstanding research on the senses of other animals, particularly on hearing in fishes. One of von Frisch's early papers was called simply "A Fish That Comes When One Whistles." And indeed he had trained a fish to do just that. However, this was only the beginning. Von

What Different Eyes See

The diagrams at right show roughly how the eyes of three animals see an object and send information about it to the brain. Each eye is shown looking at the same starlike shape from the same distance.

THE HUMAN EYE (and the eye of other advanced animals) is like a camera. It has an opening (the iris) that controls the amount of light entering the eye, a flexible lens to focus this light, and "film" (the retina at the back of the eye) to record the light. The retina picks up the star as a mosaic of many small dots (*far right*) that is received clearly in the brain.

THE OCTOPUS EYE is the most advanced of any belonging to the invertebrates (animals without backbones). Like the human eye, it works on the principle of a camera. However, the image is less sharp because the receptors in the retina are fewer and larger, producing a coarser mosaic. The image is also smaller because the eye is smaller than man's.

THE INSECT EYE is made up of many tiny eyes —as many as 28,000 in a dragonfly. Each of these eyes, which has its own lens, faces outward in a slightly different direction, taking in a slightly different scene. The diagram at far right shows how one eye, aimed directly at the star shape, receives the complete image; the surrounding eyes receive only part of it.

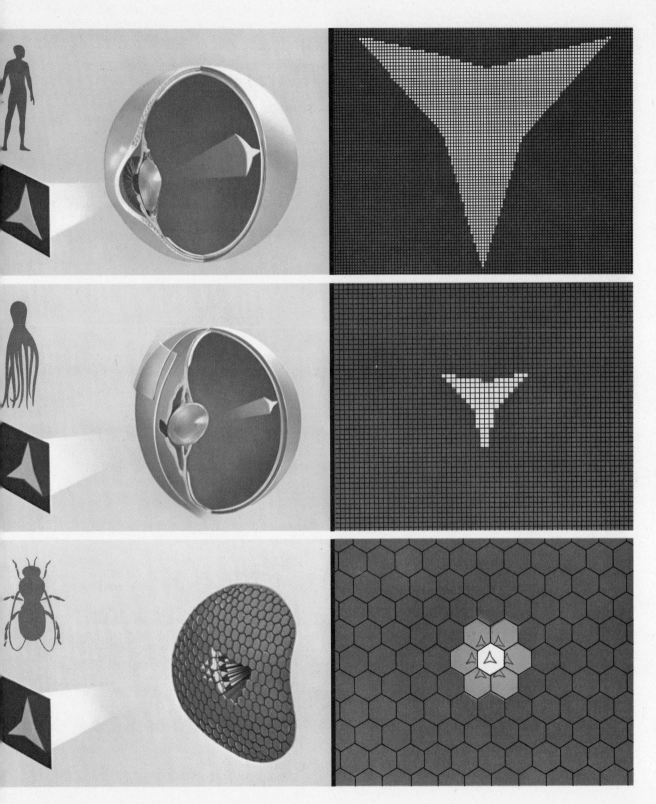

What the Octopus Sees

Experiments with octopuses show that they can tell
the difference between some shapes but not others.
Each of four shapes was presented to an octopus,
along with a crab to attract it toward food. Next, a
mild electric shock was introduced to the vertical bar
shape *(below, left)* but not to the horizontal one. The
octopus soon learned to avoid the electrified one.
However, it never could learn the difference between
the "M" and upside-down "V" shapes when one was
electrified and the other was not. This is because the
octopus' eye can only scan an object to measure its
width and height, not its exact shape. The vertical
and horizontal bars show up differently to an
octopus, but the "M" and inverted "V" look the same.

Frisch also wanted to know *why* the fish came when he whistled. His reasoning illustrates beautifully the line of research that studies of animals' senses must follow.

What stimulated the fish to come to the surface when the whistle was blown? Because we can hear, we might assume that the fish could hear too, and that it was responding to the sound. But the fish might not be able to hear. It might have just seen the movements of the man with the whistle and responded to these. How are we to know? One way is to make the same movements, but without whistling. If the fish does not come, clearly it is not movement alone that stimulates it. Or, we can whistle without moving and see whether the fish responds. Or we can block off or remove the sense organ that we think is responsible for the fish's behavior, in this case the inner ear. If the fish fails to come now, we can assume that it could hear before. Once we know that the fish can hear, we can proceed to find out what exactly its hearing organ can achieve: how well it can distinguish between different levels of pitch, or how weak the sound can be made before the animal fails to react.

Any response that an animal makes naturally—such as coming for food—can be used as an indicator of behavior. However, these natural responses are not always clear cut or easy to work with. Therefore the investigator may decide to condition or train an animal to a specific stimulus by presenting that stimulus repeatedly together with

a natural one. That is what von Frisch was doing when he whistled every time he offered food to the fish. Another way of conditioning is to flash a light every time one feeds an animal, so that it associates light and food. If the animal can see at all, sooner or later it will respond to the light alone, expecting that food will be present. This training method is widely used.

Vision is one of the five basic senses of the animal kingdom. However, not all animals see the same things. For instance, they are not all sensitive to the same colors of the spectrum. We have already noted that bees and many other insects may be sensitive to ultraviolet light, but they are far less sensitive to red. In fact, most light that we see as red is invisible to them.

But what about red flowers that are so attractive to insects? Actually, as von Frisch has pointed out, few flowers pollinated by insects are really red. Those that appear red or purple to us reflect a great deal of blue as well. And it is the blue that the insects see. Or consider that popular wild flower, the European poppy. We see it as bright red, but we also observe that it is visited by bees and other insects. A simple test will show that the poppy reflects ultraviolet light, which these insects see. We will pick two poppies and flatten them out on a board in a field where poppies grow. One is covered with a filter, a specially colored piece of glass that absorbs all visible light but transmits ultraviolet light. The

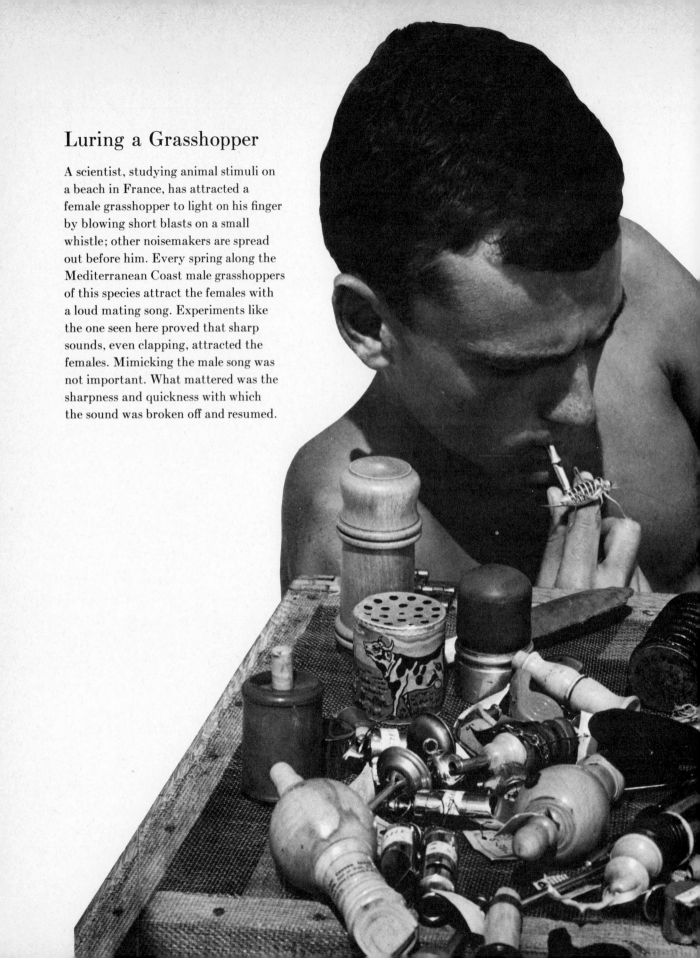

Luring a Grasshopper

A scientist, studying animal stimuli on a beach in France, has attracted a female grasshopper to light on his finger by blowing short blasts on a small whistle; other noisemakers are spread out before him. Every spring along the Mediterranean Coast male grasshoppers of this species attract the females with a loud mating song. Experiments like the one seen here proved that sharp sounds, even clapping, attracted the females. Mimicking the male song was not important. What mattered was the sharpness and quickness with which the sound was broken off and resumed.

other flower is covered with two filters—one that absorbs all visible light and one that absorbs ultraviolet light. Both flowers now appear identically black, that is, colorless to our eyes. But the insects will always alight on the first flower, responding to the reflection of the ultraviolet rays.

Can animals actually see differences in colors within the spectrum visible to them? Or do they react only to differences in brightness? This can be tested in the same way that human beings are tested for color vision. Again we use the same technique that von Frisch used in getting a fish to respond to a whistle. But this time we introduce colors as stimuli instead of sounds. Suppose, for example, that we train an animal to associate food with a red triangle by showing it such a triangle every time we offer it food. Once the animal has learned this, we then show it other triangles of the same size and shape, but of different colors: blue, green, purple, as well as shades of gray. If the animal still reacts only to the red triangle, or to a color close to red, like purple, can we then assume that it sees color? Yes, we can—almost. There is a chance that the animal is color blind and is "faking" color vision by recognizing the color as a certain shade of gray. So we make a test for its ability to recognize different shades of gray, then present it with a whole range of grays of varying shades. If the animal responds to many grays and not just to the particular one it was trained to, then we can assume that it cannot recognize differences in brightness very well. So its first response in the color test must have been a reaction to color alone. We must make sure that the animal cannot see ultraviolet or infrared light, which some of our test objects might give off.

No animal has yet been discovered that can "see" infrared light with its eyes. But there are other ways of "seeing" than with eyes alone. Infrared light is actually a form of heat, and certain creatures, notably the rattlesnake and its relatives, have organs that detect it as effectively as though they "saw" it. In front of and slightly below their eyes, the snakes have two pits; each contains a thin membrane, behind which is a cavity filled with air. The membrane is filled with many nerve endings; there are 3,500 in each tiny pit—about 100,000 times as many as humans have on an equal area of skin. Furthermore, these nerve endings are very close to the surface of the membrane. Thus a "pit viper," as such snakes are called, can sense from a foot and a half away a glass of water only a few degrees warmer than the surrounding air. Rattlesnakes will actually strike at such objects, showing that they use this sensitivity to locate warm-blooded prey. These organs not only respond to radiant heat, but they also

How the Fly Uses Its Hairs for Tasting

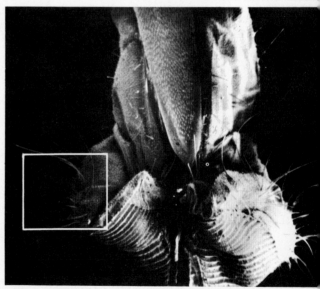

1 The housefly tastes not with a tongue, but with hairs on its feet and trunklike mouth. The fly must first step on its food to become stimulated enough to eat it. Then the fly lets down its "trunk"; the part outlined by a square is enlarged at right.

2 Magnified 75 times, the "trunk" is seen to have two lobes, or large bumps, at its tip. The fly eats by pressing the trunk against food, bits of which are drawn up through the cavity between the lobes. Part of one lobe in the square is magnified at right.

enable the snakes to detect the direction from which the heat comes. The rims of the pits act to screen out radiation from the sides; they cast heat "shadows," which of course vary with the direction from which the heat reaches the pits. These shadows, falling on the nerves of the membrane, inform the snakes where the heat source is and enable them to strike accurately.

Another point of interest in vision is the extent to which an animal can detect details. This is by no means the same in all creatures. Many worms and shellfish, for instance, have what is called a "diffuse light sense" in their skins. They see light only the way we feel warmth. All they can really do is to notice whether it is dark or light. They have at best only a very poor means of detecting where the light comes from, and they certainly cannot see objects. More advanced animals, by contrast, have developed eyes that contain an optical apparatus. Vertebrates (animals with backbones) use a lens that projects an image on a retina, a membrane at the back of the eye that is made up of millions of sensory cells, each of which contributes a tiny part to the total visual image. Insects, on the other hand, have "compound eyes"—these have no lenses but are made up of a num-

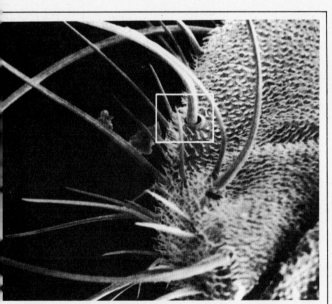

3 The area marked off by a square in the previous picture is seen as a forest of sensory hairs. Like the ones on the fly's feet, these hairs help stimulate the insect to taste, feel and eat its food. A closer picture of the hairs in the square is shown at right.

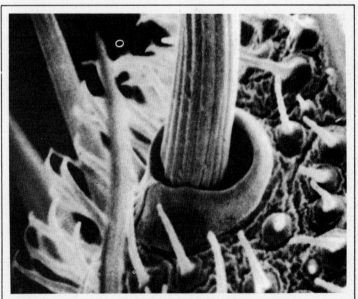

4 A single sensory hair is shown magnified almost 2,600 times by a scanning electron microscope, which allows small areas to be seen in extraordinary detail. Magnification makes the tiny hair look like a sturdy column rising from a rounded, hollow socket.

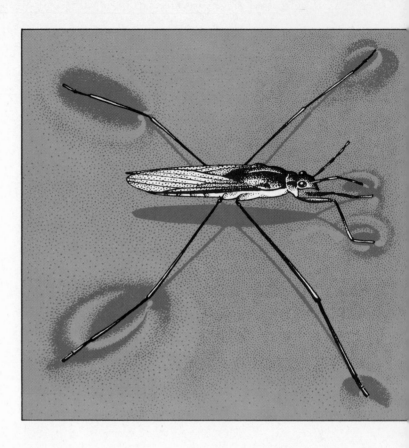

ber of cone-shaped tubes, which give the insect a wide field of vision. Each tube provides merely one point of the visual image, and all these points or dots fit together to provide a picture like a mosaic.

Sharpness of vision has, of course, many advantages. It allows predatory animals to see their prey from very far away. Insect-eating falcons are able to see single dragonflies a half a mile distant, while a man cannot see them farther away than about 100 yards. Similarly, many vulnerable animals can see their enemies from afar.

Another complex part of vision is the ability to see and recognize shapes. It is quite easy to train a bird or a mammal to respond to a circle and to ignore a rectangle. The female digger wasp, who stocks her burrow with insects she has killed as food for her larvae, has this ability. The question is, how does she manage to find her way back from some distant hunting ground to her own burrow in a large colony? I soon found that these wasps remembered the arrangement of small landmarks such as pebbles, pine cones and tufts of grass around their burrows. Knowing this, I trained wasps to recognize a circle of pine cones that I laid out around the entrance. When such a wasp went out looking for food I moved this circle a foot or so. The result

Information from Ripples

Many insects use sensory hairs to give them information about what is going on around them. The water strider *(far left)*, which feeds on smaller insects, has slender legs and a light body that enable it to skate across the water without falling in; sensory hairs on its legs pick up ripples on the surface that tell it where little insects have fallen into the water. The whirligig beetle *(left)* also glides on top of ponds. With the hairs on its front feelers it can detect ripples made by moving insects, and can even sense its own ripples bouncing off obstacles.

was that when she returned she searched vainly for her burrow in the center of the ring of cones, ignoring the real entrance, which was in plain view. In other tests, I offered her a choice between a circle of dark stones and a triangle or an oval of pine cones. Although she could tell the stones from the cones perfectly well, as I knew from other tests, she went to the stone circle—just because it was a circle.

Sense organs that respond to touch, to pressure or to other mechanical action are an important part of the basic equipment of most animals. The simplest forms occur in the skin, where they are useful in maintaining a close contact with the surrounding

environment. But mechanical stimuli of other kinds are used for far more specialized purposes. By the tension of some muscles, by the laxness of others, by the position of his bones, tendons and joints, a human being gets a constant stream of useful information about his posture and his movements. Insects have an external skeleton so that they must have other arrangements for the same purposes. Pads of sensory hairs and groups of tiny, dome-shaped organs are often found at the joint of a leg segment. In the normal position these hairs touch the next segment in such a way that any bending of the joint will move the hairs, triggering a response in the sensory nerves.

The finest development of the mechanical senses we know are the organs of hearing. Sensitivity to the various parts of the sound spectrum differs for different insects—and some can hear sounds in the ultrasonic range, which are beyond man's ability to hear. Just as bees can see ultraviolet light, moths can hear ultrasonic sound. This is an adaptation by the moths that enables them to detect their enemies, the bats, whose calls are largely ultrasonic.

The champions of hearing, by any standard, are the bats. Bat sounds long went undetected by man because they are pitched two to three octaves above what we can hear. But to a number of bats flying around on a calm, still summer evening—and to the unfortunate moths that can hear them and must try to avoid them—the evening is anything but calm. It is a madhouse of constant shrieking. Each bat sends out a series of screams in short pulses, each lasting less than a hundredth of a second.

What is important to the bat is not the sound but its echo. Bouncing off obstacles like trees, walls and flying insects, the echoes of his cries keep the bat informed of things in its way and food on the wing. This echo-location device, which acts much like the sonar employed in submarines, has evolved in different bats in different ways. Some bats send out a wide, scattered beam, others a narrow one that can be changed

Seeing What We Can't

Man has good vision, but he cannot, like some animals, "see" the extremes of the color spectrum. At left, a rattlesnake, whose eyes are taped, aims straight for a lighted, warm bulb. The snake "sees" the warm bulb just as it would a prey animal by means of a pit beneath each eye, which responds to infrared heat and guides the snake toward the warmth. At right are two pictures of the same flower. The one above is the way a man sees it. The one below was photographed through an ultraviolet filter and shows the patterns etched in ultraviolet that bees can see.

in its direction and thus used as a scanning device. We know that echo-location involves the bats' ears, mouths and, in some species, noses, because if any of these are blocked, the bats fly "blind." But how the bats' ears and brains process the information they receive from the echoes is still a mystery—their hearing equipment must be complex.

Whales use a similar "sonar" system in the water. It has long been known that whales could hear, and that they could make sounds too. British sailors called one particularly talkative species, the arctic beluga whale, the "sea canary." But the full story was not revealed until World War II, when hydrophones, developed for the detection of submarines, picked up the amazing

variety of underwater noises produced by whales and dolphins. We know now that at least some whales can transmit ultrasonic sounds as high-pitched as those of bats. But we still do not understand how they produce these sounds, since they have no vocal cords. We know also that whales use echo-location as bats do for avoiding obstacles and for finding prey, and that they have their own vocal "language."

Further investigations, like those already conducted with porpoises in the Marineland aquariums of Florida and California, may reveal still other aspects of whale life. For instance, they may explain the puzzling phenomenon of mass strandings and deaths of whales in shallow water. For many years nobody could understand why these huge creatures sometimes got stuck in the shallows and died of suffocation when the weight of their bodies, no longer supported by the water, made it impossible for them to inflate their lungs properly. Now it has been pointed out that these strandings occur almost always on gently sloping sandy or muddy bottoms. At these places the coastline apparently fails to give sharp, exact echo-location information such as the whales get on steeper, rocky coasts.

Still very mysterious are the "lateral line" organs possessed by many fishes and some frogs. These are made up of pits or grooves arranged along the body surface, each containing rows of sensory cells. From each cell protrude special sensory "hairs" that respond to the slightest movements of the surrounding water—such as those always caused by the approach of another fish. The "hairs" are extremely sensitive and, like ears, can receive information from distant objects. Because of their great sensitivity, too much stimulation actually may be painful. Many fish that are used to inhabit-

ing a certain territory ward off intruders with a strong beat of their tails; the vibrations can be as effective as direct blows.

The sound and echo-locating devices of animals are basically mechanical. But the qualities of smell and taste are often lumped together as the "chemical senses." Smell is generally used for a preliminary examination of things, sometimes at a distance. Taste is used for things actually touched, as food is tasted when it is in the mouth.

Many animals have better chemical sense organs than humans, and they use them in quite different ways. The world of smells in which a dog lives, for example, would be bewildering to a human. A good hunting dog can follow a single scent through a mixture of other scents with uncanny certainty. Mammals use smell for tracking their prey, and for avoiding their hunters. One animal with a relatively poor sense of smell may even make use of a superior nose belonging to another animal. It is a common sight in the African savanna to see baboons and impalas traveling together. The impala profits from the baboon's keen eyesight, the baboon from the impala's sense of smell.

A Spider with Eight Eyes

Most spiders spin webs to catch their prey. They cling to the webs, waiting for the strands to vibrate; their sense of touch tells them when their food is caught. But the wolf spider at right hunts for food without a web, depending on its eyes—all eight of them in this case—to help it locate meals.

SIGNALING FOR FOOD, a hungry baby herring
gull pecks at a red spot on its parent's bill. The signal
stimulates the parent to spit up food from its gullet
for the chick. This system of signs—red spot to start
pecking, pecking to spit up food—is just one example
of animals responding to signals regularly.

3

The Signs That Animals Respond To

When I am deep in a book or thinking about tomorrow's work, I may fail to hear the clock in my room tick. Yet if you were to ask me whether the clock had stopped, I would switch my attention to it and probably hear it tick very clearly.

Everyone has experienced this kind of thing. It shows that a person does not always make use of all the information his sense organs can provide. Something very similar is true of animals. Early in this century, a famous scientist, Carl von Hess, decided that all honeybees were color blind. When he took some into the laboratory and placed them in front of two lights, they always went to the brighter of the two, even though different colors were used. Von Hess concluded that the bees were reacting just like color-blind people: they chose between brightnesses rather than colors of light.

But was it really the right conclusion? Karl von Frisch, at that time a young research worker, did not think so. He felt there must be some function in the bright colors of flowers. To prove this, he performed a series of experiments with bees in their natural environment, out in a field where they were foraging, or searching for food. Instead of lights, he presented them with pieces of cardboard of various colors and also of different shades of gray. The results were clear-cut and convincing. Foraging bees did respond to colors, especially to yellow and blue. The bees tested in the laboratory, however, had not been foraging. They had been busy trying to escape; they had become unaware of color and had reacted only to the brighter light.

We know now that this is only one example of a very widespread phenomenon. Like the professor sitting in his study with the ticking clock, animals do not necessarily use all the information about the outside world that their senses are able to give them. What they do use depends on what they are doing at the moment. Therefore, if we want to understand fully how external stimuli help to control the behavior of animals, we must do more than investigate what they *can* respond to. We must find out what at any given moment they actually *do* respond to.

The behavior of the grayling butterfly provides an excellent example. Male graylings often rest on the bark of trees or on the ground in dry, sandy areas, where they are beautifully camouflaged. It is often rather startling to see one fly up out of nowhere, which it does whenever a female flies by. If the female is willing to mate, she will alight. The male then settles near her and starts his courtship. But a female that is unwilling flies on. The male, after following her a few yards, abandons her and settles down to wait for another.

What makes the male fly at the female? Simple observation in the natural habitat gave us the clue to our own line of testing. Not only the female of their own species stimulated the male graylings to rise. They flew up after a large variety of other insects, ranging in size from small flies to butterflies much larger than the female graylings. We

even saw the males rise after birds the size of thrushes. More striking still, we saw them go after falling leaves of various sizes, shapes and colors, and even chase after their own fluttering shadows.

This variety of objects that the male graylings mistook for females of their species suggested two things to us: first, that visual stimuli were important; second, that chemical stimuli were not. Scent, for example, could be ruled out on the grounds that the direction of the flights was independent of the direction of the wind.

But if the key stimulus was a visual one, how could we find out what element of vision—size, shape, color, action or a combination of these—was responsible for the graylings' behavior?

First we prepared a number of paper dummies in the shape of butterflies and attached each with a yard of thin thread to the end of a slender, three-foot pole. With these "fishing rods" we could make the

A Chick's Changing Response

When they are first born, baby songbirds respond to stimulation by stretching their necks upward and opening their mouths wide for food. If a human hand touches their nest (*far left*), they will react this way, as though a parent with food were alighting on the nest edge. Since the chicks at this point are blind, they are guided only by gravity and so stretch their necks straight up. A week later (*middle drawing*), their eyes are just open and they are able to respond to the sight of an approaching hand. But they are still controlled by gravity and still stretch straight up. They lose this trait a few days later, and from then on they will point their beaks at the hand itself (*below*).

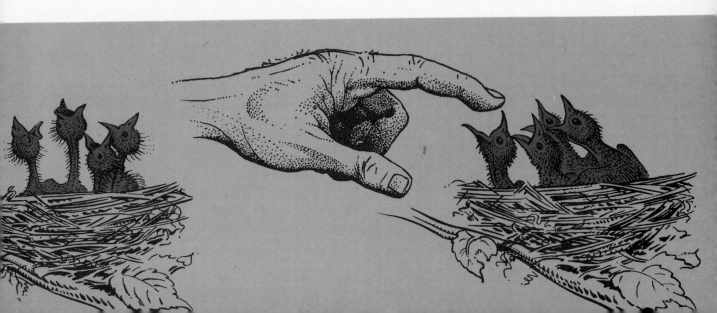

dummy butterflies do almost anything we wanted. In our first series of experiments we made them dance in the air toward a male. This always set off a vigorous response, so we took the test still further.

Next we prepared a large number of dummies, grouped in series, in which one particular part of the dummy was changed. One series, for example, consisted of dummies that were identical in all respects except color. In another, color and size were the same but the shape was varied. In still another series we changed the size. Armed with our rods and our various dummies, we roamed over the countryside searching for the male graylings. Whenever one was found, the dummies were presented.

We ran some 50,000 tests of this kind, using a large number of males found in their natural habitats. It was clear at once that the imitation of the female was not an important factor. Even when we glued the wings of a real female onto a dummy, we got no more response from it than from a dummy colored a uniform brown. Dummies of all different colors, in fact, got a response. But some seemed more effective than others. Curiously enough, it was not the natural brown of the female that worked best. Black was even better, and gradually it became clear that the darker the color of a dummy, the more effective it was. This was confirmed with a series of dummies of various shades of gray. White was least effective, and black was best.

Now what about size? We had made a series of dummies ranging from one sixth the size of a normal female to four and a half times normal size. Male graylings rose in pursuit of all these. But, much to our surprise, the larger dummies were more effective than those that were the size of an average female.

So we had established three things: movement was important, dark colors worked best, and the bigger the dummy, the better the response was. Now what about the effects of shape?

Shape, it developed, seemed of little importance. We offered many dummies of different shapes: long rectangles, butterfly shapes, circular shapes. The long rectangles were the least effective. But we found that this was not because of the shape, but because they moved differently from the other shapes—they did not flutter as well.

So the next thing we studied was the type of movement. This we did by making the same model move in different ways. As we had guessed from earlier tests, a dancing movement was about twice as effective as smooth and regular movement.

Finally, we tested the effect of distance. The same dummy was made to dance at different distances from the males. We tried this with many dummies and we found that the nearer the dummy was to the male, the more the male went after it.

Putting all this together gave us a much better understanding of why we had seen

The Wide Appeal of Babyfaces

The "baby" look of children and young animals nearly always brings on in humans the instinctive feeling of fondness a parent has for a child—and it may bring on protective and feeding responses in animals, too. In the drawings at the near left, a human infant, a bunny, a puppy and a chick all have the same kinds of features, or sign stimuli, that signal "baby": short faces, large foreheads, round eyes and plump cheeks. The larger, angular faces of the adults opposite them do not awaken the same responses. The parental feeling in humans extends not only toward children but also to such popular baby substitutes as pets and dolls.

male graylings follow birds, falling leaves, shadows and many other things that seemed so different from a female grayling. Shape mattered little to the males; nor did color. What was important was size, darkness of tone, nearness and a dancing motion. But how did all this add up for the male; in short, how did it say "female"?

The matter seemed hard to explain in human terms. So we had to consider the possibility that the male graylings "recognized" females in a way quite different from the way humans do. To us, recognition is very often the result of a "yes-no" decision of some kind. We look at something dancing past and say to ourselves "this is a female," or "this is not a female." But the butterflies showed no such clear-cut decision. They showed instead a graded scale of responses, as if many of the dummies were to them 75 per cent female or 50 per cent female. The frequency of their responses depended upon the quality of "femaleness" of the object attracting them.

One striking thing was that some prop-erties of the female, such as its color, did not seem to stimulate the males at all. Did this mean that the males were color-blind? This was hard to believe; like bees, they feed on flowers whose bright colors would seem to have some function in attracting them. We offered a series of colored dummies to graylings at a time when they were feeding—and they behaved very differently. They reacted almost exclusively to yellow and blue models. Furthermore, they did not react at all to gray models, showing that they did have true color vision. This proved to us that when graylings are feeding, they are receptive to colors. Their ability to distinguish certain colors enables them to find the "correct" flowers for their food. On the other hand, when the males are looking for a female, color is not important at all. In short, the condition of the male decides which stimuli will affect it.

Clearly, it would be interesting to see if other animals reacted in this same way. This has been done by studying a variety of behavior patterns in different animals.

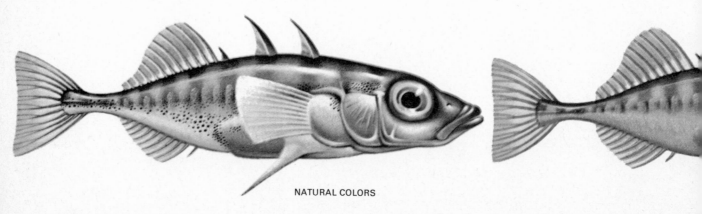

NATURAL COLORS

One of these is the feeding behavior of a large, meat-eating water beetle known as *Dytiscus marginalis*. This beetle preys on small fish, grasshoppers, worms and tadpoles, and also occasionally eats larger dead animals. The surprising thing about *Dytiscus* is its clumsiness. Although it has well-developed eyes and obviously good vision, it does not swim straight at its prey. In fact, it does not *seem* to be able to see it at all. Yet when it is near a victim it does show, by changing its normally quiet swimming into a kind of frantic thrashing, that it has become aware of it. Just what is the stimulus that prompts *Dytiscus* to chase and eat its food?

We can check this in several ways. First, we can show the beetle a tadpole enclosed in a glass test tube that we put into the water nearby. The beetle ignores the tadpole completely. It does not even make its frantic swimming movements when it touches the glass. However, if we sew the tadpole into a little bag of porous cheesecloth that hides it completely from sight,

(Text continued on page 44)

STICKLEBACK, ACTUAL SIZE

Changing Colors of Courtship

To an observer at the edge of a pond, the three-spined stickleback might seem just another small, grayish-green fish *(far left)*. But to those who have studied it in the laboratory, it provides remarkable examples of the use of sign stimuli during its reproductive cycle. The sticklebacks become ready to produce their young in the spring, when the gradual lengthening of daylight activates glands that give off hormones. Moving to shallow-water spawning grounds, the male changes its protective winter colors, exhibiting a red belly *(center picture)* to frighten other males away from the territory it has staked out. When the male has built a nest and is ready to court a female, it changes colors further, becoming bright red and blue *(below)*. How the sticklebacks use these colors and other stimuli in reproduction is shown on the following pages.

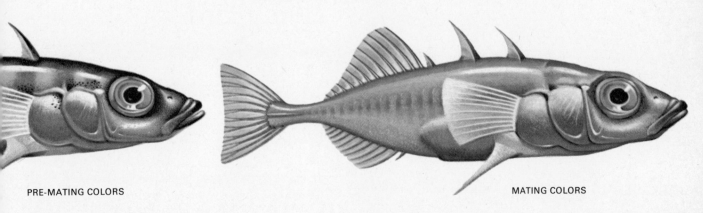

PRE-MATING COLORS

MATING COLORS

41

Reading the Vital Signs

Having built a nest from bits of weeds, the male stickleback attracts a female with its red and blue mating colors and goes into a courtship dance (*above, and 1 in key drawing at left*). The male in turn is stimulated by the female's form, which is plump with

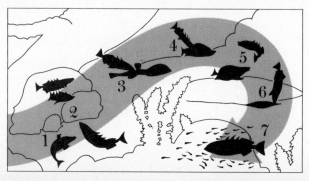

eggs, and may brush the female's belly with its stickles (2). Then the male shows the way to the nest. The male indicates the entrance by turning on its side and pointing inside with its snout (3). Once its mate has entered, the male hovers overhead, prodding the base of the female's tail with its snout, which starts the spawning (4). When the eggs are laid and the female has slipped out, the male enters the nest and fertilizes the eggs (5). The male then begins to fan water over the eggs to aerate them (6). When the brood hatches, the male, once again wearing its aggressive, pre-mating colors (7), guards the young. If they roam too far, the father picks up the strays in its mouth and spits them back into the nest.

the beetle responds vigorously. In some cases it grabs the bag with its forelegs and begins to chew it up. Or, if it happens to swim past under the bag, it immediately dives to the bottom and then swims around in irregular searching movements below. The same response can be brought on by taking water from a tank in which tadpoles have been swimming and squirting it into the water of the beetles' tank.

Obviously, when it is feeding, the beetle responds to the smell, not the sight, of its prey. Yet when it is crawling or flying about it uses its eyes to good effect to avoid obstacles, and to find bodies of water on which to alight.

Thus we see that an animal does not at any particular moment use all of the information its sense organs receive. This raises an interesting question. What happens to the stimuli it does not use? For instance, how does the beetle suppress the visual information it receives, but does not use, when feeding?

To answer this question, we have to pro-

Egg and Superegg

The herring gull on these pages is responding to a "supernormal" stimulus with amusing results. Presented with two painted wooden eggs, one of normal size and the other 20 times as large, the brooding gull inspects them closely (*far left*), then tries to incubate the giant, although it keeps falling off (*below*). To test what stimulates birds in brooding their eggs—color, markings, shape or size—scientists substituted various specimens (*left*). The important stimuli were shape and size.

gress from observation of the whole animal to a direct look at what is going on inside it. This can be done in various ways. For example, in larger animals we can sink extremely fine electrodes into a nerve center to register the very weak electrical currents generated by outside stimuli. Experiments of this kind have been carried out on cats (*below*), with an electrode sunk into a nerve center located directly behind the ear. When a metronome was made to click near the cat, it was possible to "see," electrically recorded on graphs, what the cat heard. Every time the metronome clicked the nerve center "fired" and its activity was recorded on the instruments.

When the cat was shown a mouse, however, the cat's interest at once concentrated on it. At the same instant, the brain "firing" in response to the clicks of the metronome stopped registering on the instruments, even though the metronome was still clicking as before. The cat was now unaware of what it previously had clearly heard. It had managed somehow to "shut out" the noise.

The cat with the metronome and mouse and the *Dytiscus* beetle with the swimming tadpole were both reacting to certain stimuli that they selected out of a wide range of stimuli reaching their sensory organs. These stimuli are important enough to be examined on their own. We call them "sign stimuli." It is interesting that many animals, even the higher forms, respond selectively to sign stimuli before they can have had any experience with them. This has been studied in detail, for example, in the newly hatched chicks of the herring gull.

"Tuning Out" a Stimulus

Bombarded constantly by different sights, sounds and other stimuli, animals must be able to choose the ones that are most useful at the moment. A cat sitting quietly will hear the ticking of a metronome behind it; if an electrode is placed in the cat's head and wired to a meter, the cat's response to the regular ticking can be read on a graph (*right*). But if the cat sees a mouse (*far right*), the sound of the metronome will no longer register; as the graph shows, the ticks have now been "tuned out." The stimulus of a possible meal has captured all the cat's attention.

Normally, as soon as they are hungry, these chicks peck at a red patch near the tip of the yellow bills of their parents. It is this red patch itself that brings on the pecking reaction. A yellow bill without the red patch stimulates only a quarter of the responses and patches of other colors score somewhere in between. Even when one presents the chicks with an array of colored bills, all get the same response—except a red bill, which is twice as effective. Yellow, the natural color of the parents' bills, scores no higher than white, black or blue. But a chick will peck at a red cherry, and I was even told of one case when a fully grown young gull ran up to a little girl at the seashore and pecked vigorously at a red scab on her knee!

This kind of reaction is what we call "mis-firing." An animal's behavior may "go off" under the wrong circumstances and fail to attain the proper goal. Such misfires often indicate that an animal is responding to a sign stimulus. Whenever a cuckoo chick is placed in a songbird's nest, the songbird's behavior misfires: it feeds the larger chick and ignores its own chicks. Our knowledge of sign stimuli tells us why this happens. The cuckoo looks very different from the bird's own young, but it has the equipment that matters. It has a large mouth that it holds wide open to show its brightly colored throat, stimulating the parent to feed it. The cuckoo chick, therefore, survives because the songbird's behavior is misfiring. In the same way, a moth that has big "eye-spots" on its wings survives because these "eyes" stimulate the songbird to fright—

A "Mother's" Touch

The stimulation of warmth and comfort provided by contact with a mother is vital to young animals, as experiments with rhesus monkeys show. In tests conducted at the University of Wisconsin, Harry F. Harlow presented new-born rhesus monkeys with two artificial "mothers"—one with a wire frame, wooden face and feeding bottle (*left*), the other with a terry-cloth covering. Harlow discovered that the baby monkeys preferred the warm, soft "cloth mother," even when the wire one offered the babies food and the cloth one did not (*below*).

they alone are the effective stimuli, no matter what the rest of the moth may look like.

The study of stimuli has its practical side too, but we are not making much use of it. For example, recordings of birds giving their calls of danger have been employed to frighten birds away from airport runways where they endanger the planes. Similar calls could scare birds from fields of crops far more effectively than scarecrows. The U.S. Department of Agriculture has also made good progress in the use of sex and food stimuli both to locate and control destructive insects like the gypsy moth in New England and the Mediterranean fruit fly in Florida.

Most experiments on sign stimuli have been carried out with dummies whose design was based on the natural object. The idea was that the natural object would be the most strongly stimulating one. But, as we have already seen, the grayling male was not by any means most strongly stimulated by dummies of normal female size, but large models were better and black dummies were more effective than the naturally colored brown ones. In other words, we have found we can improve on nature. We can provide "supernormal stimulation." Several such cases have been well studied. Gulls and other birds, if offered the choice between an egg of normal size and a larger egg, will choose the larger one. But this choice tricks them. They find that, in spite of frantic attempts, they cannot even sit on the oversized egg. Herring gull chicks, as we have seen, peck at the red spot on the bill of their parent. But further tests showed that this was not a color stimulus alone but also a matter of contrast. The chicks also pecked at dummy bills showing strongly contrasting patches, such as very white spots on very dark bills or very dark spots on very light bills. And probing still further, we found that the chicks responded to the shape of the bill too: a thin bill brought more responses than a thick bill.

With all this information in hand, we decided to try another improvement on nature. We made a thin rod and colored it red; then we painted three bright white rings on it. To the human eye this did not look at all like a good imitation of a herring gull's bill. Yet the chicks aimed 25 per cent more pecks at it than at a real herring gull's bill! Thus the artificial bill had something that stimulated the chicks to peck at it, something more compelling than the parent's bill with its red dot.

This phenomenon of "supernormality" may well be more widespread than we realize. For instance, it is possible that many songbirds are not merely *willing* to feed a young cuckoo but actually *love* to feed it, just because the cuckoo offers such an enormous and inviting mouth. And the curious fact that several species of hawk moth caterpillars have not one but two eyespots on each side of their bodies may have a similar explanation. To the songbirds that feed on them this supernormal arrangment may be more frightening than a normal set of eyes.

Can any of this be applied to man? Since it is not always easy to experiment on our own species, we know less about ourselves than we do about some animals. But there are many indications that we, too, are sensitive to supernormal stimulation. Many of the animals in the widely beloved cartoons of Walt Disney—Mickey Mouse, Donald Duck and others—have "supernormal" babyfaces that stimulate a feeling of affection in us; so do the characters in the popular comic strip "Peanuts."

When we study sign stimuli in greater detail, we see that neither they nor the responses they generate are as simple as they might appear. The following story shows how complex a simple stimulus can be.

Young thrushes, when they are about 10 days old, begin to point their gaping mouths at the head of the parent bird. It can be easily shown with dummies that any slightly moving object close to and above the young birds makes them gape. If we use as a dummy a flat, circular disk—something that has no top or bottom but will look the same no matter how it is turned—we find that the little birds gape at the highest part of the disk, the part where the parent's head normally ought to be. But if we add a piece that sticks out from the disk, this becomes the "head" for the baby bird—even if it is placed near the bottom of the disk where no normal head should be. The shape of the extra piece does not seem to matter, but its size does. And this is most interesting —it is *relative* size, not *absolute* size, that counts. If the "head" is almost as large as the "body," apparently it does not seem like a head and is not as effective as a smaller head would be. This is tested by presenting a disk with two "heads" of different sizes. The small birds will gape at the one with the most lifelike proportions; they will stretch toward the larger of the two heads when both are attached to a large body,

A Shelter from the Tide

The first ripple of the returning tide on the beach is a signal to the air-breathing soldier crab of tropical Asia to build its own shelter against the incoming water and predatory fish. The crab starts by forming a shallow crater *(far left)*, then pushes pellets of wet, muddy sand up on either side until it has built a roof over its head. The crab then burrows deeper, loosening more sand and plastering it overhead to form a sturdy roof. The completed shelter provides a life-giving bubble of air inside *(below)*.

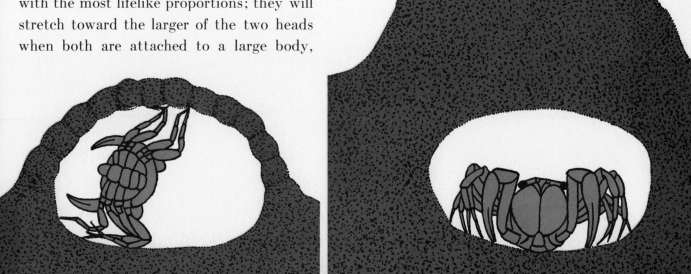

and to the smaller head when they are attached to a smaller body.

We began this chapter by considering what seemed to be a rather simple problem: to which outside stimuli does an animal actually react? We end it on a note of great complexity. We have seen that not all the information which the sense organs can provide is used by the brain. Part of the "input" of stimuli that goes into the animal is somewhere made ineffective, depending on what the animal is doing. We have further seen that even the simpler kinds of information, the "sign stimuli," depend on how the animal uses them.

What the animal finally achieves seems to be much more primitive than what humans do. Animal behavior "misfires" much more strikingly than our own behavior does. But we must not forget that most of this misfiring occurs when we ourselves disturb the animal's normal environment. However risky it might seem for an animal to rely on stimuli, the *actual* risk is not great, and we have to admit that the system works remarkably well.

A Strong Maternal Instinct

A hen, deprived of its own chicks, continues reacting to maternal stimuli by taking two kittens under its wings. The kittens, in turn, seem quite happy, but although they played about with the hen and licked its feathers, they eventually abandoned their foster mother to grow up in the ways of cats.

WILD AND STRANGE are the mating antics of these Tibetan barheaded geese high on a mountain lake. This wingspreading ritual takes place after the birds have mated in the water. Usually both birds spread their wings, although in this picture it is the male alone, rising breathtakingly behind its mate.

4
The Machinery That Makes Things Go

We know that animals are keenly aware of, and react sharply to, the sights, sounds, smells and other so-called "outside stimuli" that surround them all the time. But we also know that their behavior must be controlled from within.

One everyday fact alone makes this obvious: a hungry dog offered a steak will gobble it down, while an animal with a full stomach will usually refuse even the most tempting food. This points up a general rule: an animal's reaction to the same stimulus, depending on the conditions, may range from a full response to none at all. We also find that at some times a very strong stimulus is needed to get a reaction, while at other times an animal responds to only the slightest stimulus.

Sometimes animals may even act a cer-

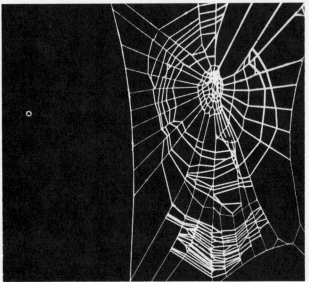

Drugs at Work on Spiders

Animal as well as human behavior can be strikingly altered by the use of drugs. The picture above shows a researcher squeezing a drop of dope on the web of a spider, who eats it. Instead of spinning a normal web *(below)*, a spider under the stimulation of a "pep" drug is too impatient to circle the web's center and concentrates on one area *(top right)*. Caffeine, a drug found in coffee, makes the spider spin a haphazard tangle of threads *(right)*. A "knockout drop" of chloral hydrate puts the spider to sleep after it has completed only a small part of its web *(bottom right)*.

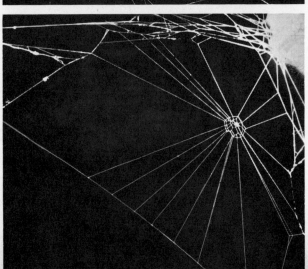

tain way without any of the stimuli normally associated with such an act. For example, flies always preen their wings whenever dust particles stick to them; but why is it that flies without wings, like certain freak species, also make these special wing-cleaning movements regularly?

This type of behavior may seem spontaneous, that is, happening without any apparent reason. We cannot see any outside stimulus that could possibly cause a fly to clean wings it does not have. But just because we cannot see a reason does not mean that it is not there. Internal factors must have caused the fly to preen its wings. This brings us deep into the study of the animal's own internal makeup.

Among the best-known agents of internal stimulus are the hormones. These "chemical messengers" are released into the blood by the endocrine glands, and they influence many behavior patterns. For instance, the sex glands of advanced animals produce sex hormones that are necessary to make an animal show its full sexual behavior. If their sex glands are removed, stopping the flow of sex hormones, roosters neither crow nor mate, nor do male sticklebacks build nests. But when such animals are injected with the male sex hormone, they will once again take on the behavior patterns of normal males with glands intact.

So far-reaching are the effects of hormones that their study has grown into a science called endocrinology. It is now known that reproductive behavior, for instance, is controlled by a variety of hormones. Some of these hormones are given off by the sex glands, and others by the pituitary, a tiny gland near the brain. Some of the pituitary hormones stimulate the sex glands to produce their sex hormones in the first place, and the two together have a great variety of effects. In most cases, full sexual behavior, including courtship, fighting and guarding the nest, will occur in most animals only when both the pituitary hormones and the sex hormones are supplied in the correct order.

Other internal stimuli are provided by nerve cells called "sense receptors." Mammals urinate when sense receptors in the wall of the bladder respond to increasing tension as the bladder fills up. Similarly, breathing quickens when the respiratory centers located in the back part of the animal's brain signal that there is too much carbon dioxide in the blood and that more oxygen is needed.

When we speak of internal control of behavior we are speaking only of the events that happen just before the behavior. These events, however, are often themselves controlled by the environment. The internal control of reproductive behavior, for example, is regulated by hormones, substances manufactured and released by the pituitary gland at the base of the brain, and by the sex glands. Yet this manufacture, or secretion, of hormones is in part controlled by external events such as the time of year. Many animals of the northern Temperate Zone, if kept artificially under the light conditions of a typical short winter day, will not show the normal spring activity of the sex glands even though the season may be far advanced. But when the same animals are subjected to increasing day lengths or kept in a constant artificial "day" of 16 hours of light and eight hours of darkness, their sex glands will begin to make and give off hormones. The animals in these tests may even reproduce in midwinter.

The effect of such hormones on behavior is not simple. Pigeons offer a case in point. They feed their young in an unusual way, by spitting up "crop milk," a substance rich in proteins given off by glands in the throat. These glands are not active in the winter, but become active in the spring when the pituitary gland begins to release a hormone called prolactin. Prolactin starts the process of milk production in the pigeon. But the mother does not actually begin to spit up the milk until its young press against its breast. This act of pressing is an outside stimulus signaling that the young are now ready to be fed.

Behavior, then, is controlled by external stimuli, or by the working of internal organs, or—as is usually the case—by a combination of both. Let us now look at the actual behavior patterns that result from such stimuli. Examined in detail, these patterns reveal themselves as marvelous, com-

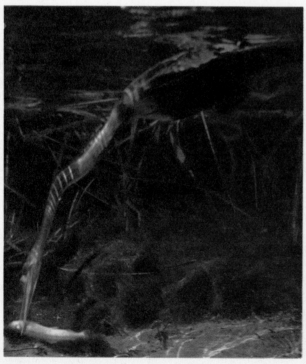

plex sequences of large and small events. The reproductive behavior of many birds, for example, begins in the spring with a male settling on a territory and driving off rivals. It continues with a female joining him, and then progresses to mating, nest building, incubation of the eggs and, finally, rearing of the young. All of this is started by the fact that the spring days are getting longer, and the greater amount of daylight stimulates the bird's pituitary gland. But this reaction of the pituitary is only the first step. To understand the full sequence, we also need to know how the bird is made to switch into the right phase at the right time as the cycle of behavior progresses.

Let us see how this works in one part of the reproductive sequence, nest building.

A Pattern for Fishing

The anhinga, a long-necked, long-billed wading bird that dives for fish, has a set behavior routine for catching its meals. As it floats on the water surface, it spreads its wings, casting a shadow that cuts the sun's glare from its eyes and attracts fish to the shade. Then the anhinga dives to catch them (*far left*). Once it has a fish in its bill, the anhinga flips it in order to gulp it down headfirst (*below*). The bird never swallows the fish tailfirst; going down that way, the scales and fins would catch and tear at its throat.

Female canaries, like many other songbirds, build their nests in two phases. The main cup is built first, of grass and other collected bits and pieces, and then it is lined with feathers. As the building progresses, the birds gradually collect less grass and more feathers. Now, we know that the building behavior as a whole is under the control of hormones; birds can be made to build nests out of season by injections of the female sex hormone, estrogen. The switch from grass to feathers, however, is not directly to hormone action, but to external stimuli. In plain language, when the female sits in the nest between bouts of collecting, it gets scratched by the grass.

Ordinarily the female would not be so sensitive to the feel of the nest. But as egg-laying time approaches it begins to lose feathers from its underside, which results in a bare piece of skin known as the "brood patch." This well-timed shedding of feathers is caused by hormone action, which, in turn, is sparked by two special stimuli— the presence of the male canary and the building of the nest cup.

All these factors combine to produce the brood patch, which then begins to receive an increased blood supply so that the female will be able to warm its eggs as it sits on them. This development also makes the brood patch increasingly sensitive to the touch, and so the stimulus received from the nest becomes stronger, and this stronger stimulus somehow makes the female switch to collecting feathers. By lining the cup with this soft material the bird essentially reduces the stimulus provided by the nest to a lower, and less important, level.

This is only one of the many processes that control the orderly performance of reproductive behavior. The entire machinery is a wonder; all parts work beautifully together. Hormone secretion and external stimuli interact continuously and in such a harmonious way that at each step the required behavior is produced.

Even within one step, or phase, there are complex patterns of behavior. A nest-building bird sets out to search for nest material, finds it, picks it up, tests it perhaps, and either rejects it or accepts it. Then it flies to the nest, deposits it there and works it into the existing structure through a series of special movements. It may push the building material into the nest's rim, sit down on the nest, then trample with its feet so as to mold the nest cup. When this is done, it begins the cycle again, setting out once more to collect the next bit of material.

Much of the natural behavior of animals consists of cycles that are really series of simple acts. We know in several cases how these so-called "action chains" are controlled. The first stage is usually spontaneous. For example, internal changes cause a hungry animal to set out to search for food without having yet seen any food. This initial searching phase, often called "appetitive behavior," is controlled from within. But

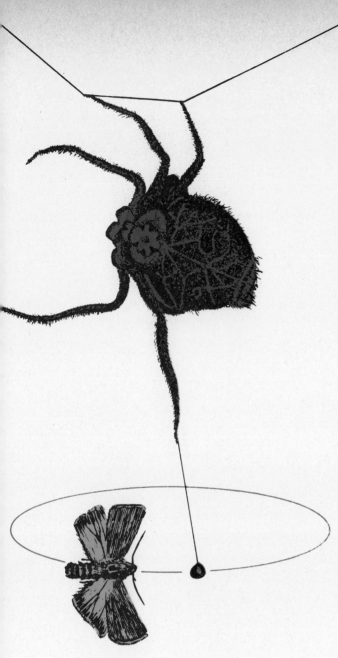

A Spider That "Fishes"

Instead of spinning a full web to trap its prey, the hairy imperial spider of Australia "fishes" for its food in mid-air. The spider first spins a horizontal thread, from which it hangs. Then it lowers another thread with a sticky drop on its end and swings it in a circle, waiting for an insect to fly past. The insect is either attracted by the motion of the lure or an odor given off by the spider. Whatever the reason, the insect is tempted to fly in close, only to become stuck on the drop and be hauled in by the spider.

the switch from this to the next phase, and to the phases that follow, is often caused by external stimuli.

The female digger wasp provides some excellent illustrations of such switches. When this wasp goes out hunting, it begins by flying to a field where honeybees are feeding on flowers. Bees are among the wasp's favorite foods and it moves from plant to plant until it spots one. When this happens, the wasp flies straight at the bee and takes up a position three or four inches downwind from it. The entire hunt so far has been visually controlled, that is, the wasp has found its victim by eye. But at this point the wasp apparently does not yet recognize the bee as a bee. A fly or even a chip of wood dangling in a spider's nest will make the wasp fly toward it and take up its position in readiness to attack.

Now, however, we enter a new phase of the cycle. The wasp hovers in position for a few seconds and then suddenly leaps at its prey. The leap is brought on by the scent of the bee, which serves to identify the bee exactly for what it is. If the wasp has been attracted by another insect—or even by an odorless dummy we have placed in its hunting area—it will not leap; after a few seconds of hovering it will leave the false prey. But if we have given the dummy a bee's scent by rubbing it against a real honeybee, the wasp will leap and seize it. The wasp will also leap at dead bees dangled in front of it. But it will not leap at a bee

Three Acts to Kill a Bee

When a female digger wasp sets out to hunt a bee for food, its actions are controlled by a series of different outside stimuli. The wasp cruises in zigzag fashion until it spots what looks like a bee on a flower *(below, left)*. But its eyesight alone is not enough to identify the insect as a bee. So the wasp places itself downwind from its target and pauses for an instant while another sense comes into play—smell. If the object smells like a bee, the wasp grabs it. Finally, if it feels like a bee, the wasp stings it to death *(right)*.

WIND DIRECTION

that has been de-scented by being dipped into a bath of ether.

The leap is normally followed by the wasp rapidly turning the bee around so they are face to face. The wasp then stings the bee under the chin, killing it. Again, this next act is started by a different stimulus, in this case a sensation of touch. If a dummy is used at this stage, it must not merely look like a bee and smell like a bee but it must also *feel* like a bee. A scented stick, for example, will not be stung, but a dead fly that has been given a bee scent will be, because it *feels* like a bee.

At each of these switches from one act to the next, the animal responds to specific stimuli. But even when these stimuli come from the same object, the animal at each stage selects certain of them and ignores

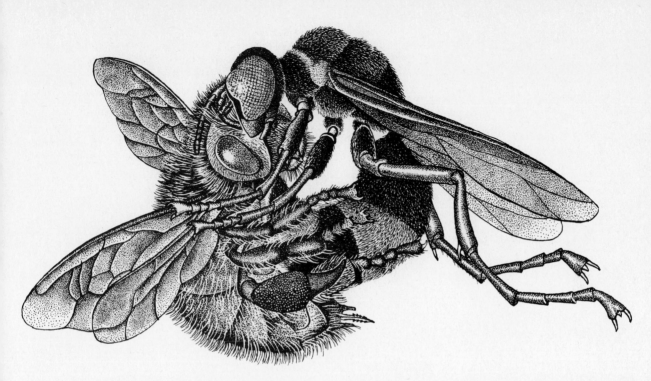

others. It is clear that the mechanism controlling this selection changes from moment to moment as an animal advances through the behavior pattern.

By this time, we have gone quite far in our discussion of behavioral activities. We are now at the point where we can begin to consider individual phases of movement, like walking, swimming and flying. But these, too, are complicated sequences of events that must be pulled apart and studied. What makes an animal move its feet in a regular rhythm to carry it over the ground? What makes a fish's fin sweep back and forth in a regular right-left sequence? How is the up-and-down alternation of a bird's wing controlled?

The individual acts of a behavior chain, once started, can often run their full course without outside control. An animal that starts to run, triggered by the stimulus of wanting to escape, can continue running for a long time even without further stimulation. The urge to escape is great enough to dominate any less important signs that might make the animal stop. Even a hungry animal, fleeing from an enemy, will seldom stop to feed at the sight of even the most tempting food.

More complicated acts of behavior may also be carried to their conclusion automatically. When the grayling butterfly, for example, has found a willing female, it starts an elaborate courtship ritual. This ends with an elegant bow in which the male spreads its wings, moves them far forward and then, catching the female's antennae between them, presses them slowly together. This act brings the male's scent-producing organs, which lie on the upper surface of its

A Stance to Scare Enemies

Baboons are hunted by large meat-eating animals like leopards. But they are good at defending themselves and adopt a fierce stance that reminds a would-be attacker they can fight back. With teeth bared and the hair around its neck raised, the baboon stamps the ground aggressively to discourage its enemy.

forewings, in contact with the female's organs of smell, which are located on the antennae. The resulting chemical stimulus starts the mating behavior.

But the male will court a dead female too. Not only that, but once the male has started its courting bow, the female can be removed and the male will go right on through the entire ritual. Only when the male has completed the bowing activity, which marks the end of the "ceremony," will it start searching about for the female, which had already been taken away.

So far, we have been considering only what makes an animal start a particular kind of behavior. But what makes it stop? One of the striking things about living creatures is that they do no more than is required. Unlike machines, they do not have to be switched on and off; something is built into an animal's system that does this at the proper time.

In some cases, of course, an outside agent stops one kind of behavior simply by providing a strong stimulus that triggers some quite different behavior. The appearance of an enemy, for instance, will make most animals stop their feeding and start fleeing or crouching instead. Usually, however, an animal stops an activity like feeding of its own accord. Life processes are self-regulating; the animal maintains a basically steady state, doing neither too much nor too little. We have learned from electronics engineers that such a state can be maintained only if processes stop themselves when they are no longer required. This is done by "negative feedback," to use the engineers' term. This "feedback" slows down the process and, if necessary, brings it to an end.

A familiar example of "negative feedback" is furnished by the oil burner and thermostat that regulates the temperature in a house. The burner has only two modes of operation—on and off. When the burner is on, the room warms up until a preset temperature is reached; at this point the thermostat cuts off the electricity so that the burner stops. In other words, the feedback from the results of the burner's "on" mode turns it off. When the room has cooled to a certain point, the thermostat turns the burner on again, and so it alternates between on and off.

Essentially, then, negative feedback involves the constant correction of errors or changes. The "machine" involved in the behavior of animals, of course, is much more complicated than the combination of oil burner and thermostat. But the principle is the same. Our task, as students of behavior, is to find out just how this behavior machinery prevents an animal from "overdoing it," and what controls are at work checking the animal's actions.

A simple example is the feeding behavior of most mammals. There are many possible consequences of eating that could tell an animal when it has had enough. But more than anything else it is the actual filling of

SUBSTITUTE ACTION

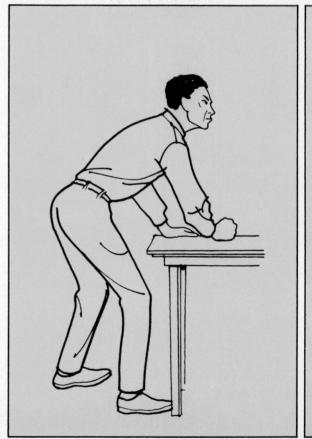

Reacting to Conflicts

Birds, men and other animals react much the same way when they are urged ahead by anger but at the same time held back by fear or other emotions. A starling (*left*), facing a rival, may preen its feathers instead of fighting; a man faced with a similar situation might scratch his head in frustration (*below*). When a gull (*center*) cannot complete any of several acts, it stands ready to peck but unable to strike; a man might clench his fists and take a step forward. To release feeling, the blackbird at far left pecks furiously at a leaf instead of at a bird, just as an angry man might react by banging his fist on a substitute target like a table.

FROZEN ANGER

FRUSTRATION

the stomach that stops the feeding process.

This was proved in a series of experiments with rats. Tubes were inserted in the throats of one group of test rats in such a way that food could be siphoned off as fast as it was eaten, before it reached the stomach. In another group, food was put into the rats' stomachs through the same kind of tubes, without being taken in normal fashion through the mouth.

As always in such tests, a "control" group of rats fed normally was used for comparison. These rats were given certain amounts of food, which they ate in the regular way. The test animals, meanwhile, were given the same amounts of food, except that in one group the food never reached the stomach but was drawn off through the tubes; in the other group of rats the food was pushed directly into their stomachs without their going through the motions of eating it. All three groups of rats were offered food a short time later. The degree of fullness of each was judged from the amount that they would eat. Not surprisingly, the animals that had "eaten" without having filled their stomachs were prepared at once to eat normally. But both the animals that had eaten normally and those whose stomachs had been filled from the outside showed every sign of being full. The same reaction was produced even when a rat's stomach was filled not with food but with a special, non-nourishing bulk that could not be absorbed. We must therefore conclude that the presence of substance in the stomach, whether it is food or not, produces a stimulus that removes the urge to feed.

So far, we have been analyzing one kind of behavior at a time and trying to piece together how each is controlled. But with so very many behavior patterns an animal could use, how does it happen that it actually uses only one at a time?

First of all, "mixed" behavior in most cases is physically impossible; for example, an animal obviously cannot approach and go away from the same object at the same time. On the other hand, a feeding antelope, startled by the scent of a lion, could try to snatch leaves off the bushes as it dashes away from the danger spot—yet it does not. Why? This is clearly a case of internal control. However hungry the antelope is, and however tempting the food may be, it stops responding to these normally powerful stimuli and flees.

Exactly how one major behavior pattern overcomes another is practically unknown. A beginning of an analysis has been made in some simple cases, and there are indications that strong stimulation of one behavior system holds back all other behavior systems through connections within the central nervous system. But the mechanics of this remain to be discovered.

There are many times, however, when an animal is strongly stimulated in various ways at once, and when neither of the two, or even three, behavior patterns involved

A "Brood Patch" Is Formed

When a female canary is ready to reproduce, the feathers on its breast are shed to form a "brood patch" of bare skin, shown here being probed for sensitivity. The brood patch, which keeps eggs warm while hatching, is the result of sex hormones, an internal stimulus. But the production of hormones, in turn, is started by external stimuli (see next page).

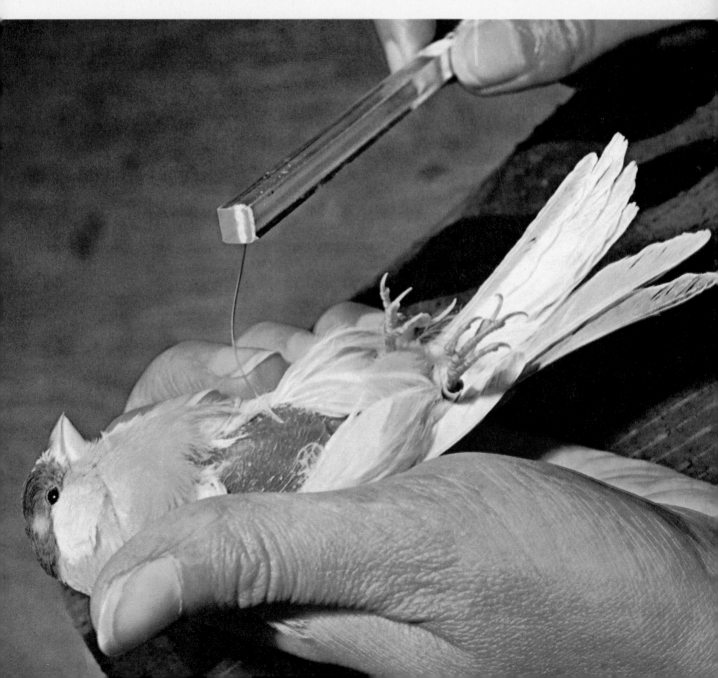

The Forces
behind Mating

In order to reproduce successfully, a canary must find a mate, build a nest, lay its eggs, hatch them and feed the young. This seems easy enough, but it really involves a number of behavioral changes, each of which must happen at the right time and in the right order. Some of these are the result of external stimuli, such as sunlight or the presence of a male. Others come from within the female. The cycle of changes is shown in simplified form in the diagram on these two pages. For clarity, the phases are seen as separate steps. Actually, the cycle is a continuous process —some forces increase while others slack off.

1 The warm spring sun activates both the male and female canaries' sex glands to produce hormones. This makes the male sing and show off (*below*), which acts as a stimulus (*arrow*) to the female.

2 The continued stimulation of the male's presence causes the female to collect material for the nest. The tiny eggs growing in the bird's ovaries (*circle*) now begin to increase rapidly in size.

3 Next the female begins to shed feathers from its breast to form a brood patch. This bare area of sensitive skin now comes in direct contact with the nest, providing the female with a stimulus (*arrow*).

70

wins out over the others. In such cases we observe "conflict behavior." One example is the display of threatening put on by a male bird facing a rival. The male is at the same time stimulated to attack and to flee —it is aggressive as well as afraid. It displays this behavior most often right on the boundary of its territory, just where fear of its opponent prevents it from advancing any farther. Such "threat postures" have been produced experimentally in geese by presenting two sets of stimuli together: those that normally make the geese flee, and those that make them attack. These and other conflict movements are of great interest because they are often "understood" by other animals—they act as signals and as such form the basis of a useful and vitally important animal "language."

We have come a long way since we began to ask simply why an animal behaves the way it does. We have seen that behavior, then, is controlled in a great variety of ways, from the outside and from within. Outside stimuli are let in carefully, depending on the internal condition of the animal. This information in the animal is used in complicated ways. Movements are produced by beautifully coordinated muscle contractions. The internal state of the animal changes from month to month, from hour to hour, from second to second. With each change the animal is not only made to perform different movements but also to "open the gate" to selected stimuli. Different parts of the behavior machinery keep each other

4 After mating with the male, the female's hormone action enlarges the oviduct, the tube through which the eggs will be laid. Meanwhile, enlarged blood vessels turn the brood patch a bright red.

5 The sensitivity of the brood patch now stimulates the female to line the nest with soft feathers. The combined stimuli of the nest and female body hormones cause the eggs to move to the oviduct.

6 The female starts to lay eggs at the rate of one a day for several days. The stimulus of the brood patch touching the nest causes the female to do most of the brooding, while the male stands guard.

71

in check and struggle for dominance. Whatever an animal does, at the crucial points "negative feedback" prevents the animal from overdoing it.

Yet our exact knowledge of all these intricate processes is still extremely slight. The machinery is being studied in many ways. Some scientists are watching the behavior of animals in the wild to find out what kinds of things the machinery must do so that the animal can behave properly. Other scientists are trying to "take apart" the machinery itself in the laboratory. The processes in nerve cells and in centers and circuits are being studied, and attempts are being made to see how these processes could produce the behavior the animal performs. As yet the two fields of research have not really made contact. Scientists studying the physical processes within single nerve cells have found them to be much more complicated than was believed even 20 years ago. Students of the behavior of the whole animal are also beginning to realize that their studies have at best provided only the barest sketch of the way the complex structure of behavior is organized.

A Dance to Woo Males

Only rarely in the animal world do females take the aggressive role in courting. But an excellent example of those that do are female ostriches, seen here high-stepping in Kenya, East Africa, in an attempt to lure nearby males. Ostriches are especially ungainly, but their courtship dance is surprisingly graceful.

5

How Animals Find Their Way About

If you were caught in a sudden blizzard on the plains or a cloudburst in the forest, you might well decide that it was time to go home. However, you might find that in the howling storm you would soon lose your way. No matter how good a walker you might be, you would never get home unless you were also able to orient yourself —that is, to know exactly where you were.

This is a simple illustration of a basic rule that is true of all animals: to be effective, behavior has to be controlled in space as well as time. Animals have to be able to find their home territory, food, a resting place, a mate and many other things. They have to move away from enemies. In short, they must know where to go and where to be, and where not to go or be. They also have to keep their bodies properly positioned in space. We take it for granted that we stay right side up, but actually part of our behavioral machinery is constantly at work keeping us that way.

Many animals are capable of truly astonishing feats of orientation. The classic example is the migration of birds. Even the young birds of some species, despite their

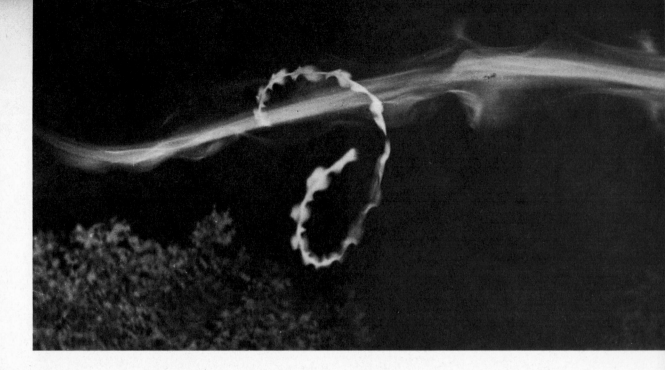

lack of experience, can travel long distances all on their own. How does a young wheat-ear bird, hatched in the summer in far northern Greenland, find its way through lonely nights of flying to countries thousands of miles to the south in Africa? How do the petrels that breed on Tristan da Cunha, and in the fall scatter over all the vast Atlantic, find their way back to their tiny island in the spring? Nor are these even the most spectacular of known migrations. Certain eels from the Atlantic seaboards of both North America and Europe travel in the darkness of the ocean depths to spawning grounds 1,200 feet down in the Sargasso Sea. Their offspring drift all the way back, each to its own coast, and manage to find the fresh-water streams and lakes many miles inland that are their habitat. Salmon do the opposite, traveling back from the ocean to spawn in the particular river where they grew up years before.

These are peak achievements of orientation, but actually they differ only in degree from more everyday examples of animals finding their way about. Birds of prey will fly straight to hunting grounds where they had success the day before. A sea gull flying from its nest to its feeding ground follows a flight path that leads it from one updraft to another over the tops of the hills—a path that varies with the direction of the wind. A fish, swimming in a dim world that to us seems to have no up or down, still knows where "up" is.

Orientation is an ever-present necessity. In fact, very few behavior patterns are not oriented. And it is a very complex business indeed. Rarely, for instance, do fins, wings or legs on both the right and left sides of an animal act with equal muscular force. Thus, if animals did not have external guidance, their movements would make them move crazily or in circles. A regular course cannot be steered or a constant position maintained without continuous checking and correcting, just as a plane must be

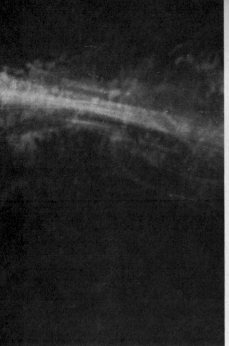

Hunting Moths by "Sonar" in the Dark

A keen sense of orientation is as important for hunting as it is for navigation. Bats hunt with the same echo-location equipment that enables them to find their way through a complicated maze. Following the echoes reflected from a moth, the bat may easily catch it in one pass; this is seen in the picture above, in which a bat (*long streak*) picks off a moth that is frantically spiraling in an attempt to escape. In the multiple-flash photograph at right, a bat catches a moth but drops it (*bottom*) when it finds the moth is not good to eat.

steered with constant corrections through wind currents when it comes in to land.

On some occasions, however, animals behave like a man firing a gun, checking or "aiming" first and then "pulling the trigger." Once the bullet has left the gun its direction cannot be corrected. This is what the praying mantis and the chameleon do when they strike at their prey. Similarly a lurking pike, when it sees a small fish approaching, aims itself exactly and then darts forward, with probably no chance to correct its forward rush once it has started.

In a few cases it has actually been demonstrated that a movement is controlled by two entirely different mechanisms acting at the same time. Like a ship pushed through the water by its propeller and guided by its rudder, an animal may be governed by one mechanism that says when a movement shall take place and with what force and for how long, and another mechanism that guides the direction of the movement.

An example of this is the behavior of ground-breeding birds when an egg accidentally rolls out of the nest.

Correcting such an accident can clearly be a tricky problem, since an egg, being slightly lopsided, rolls unpredictably even on smooth and level ground. What the bird does is quite wonderful to see. Sitting on

How a Wasp Uses Landmarks

A digger wasp always memorizes the landmarks around its burrow so that it will be able to find its way back. In an experiment to test this, the author of this book placed a ring of pine cones around a burrow (*right*), and the wasp immediately learned to recognize it. But when the ring was moved a foot or two (*center drawing*), the wasp could not find the burrow just outside the ring. When the cones were rearranged in a triangle and a decoy ring of pebbles was made (*far right*), the wasp chose the pebbles. This proved it was the shape of the arrangement rather than the cones that the insect was responding to.

the nest, it stretches its head forward until its bill reaches beyond the egg. Then, with constant, tiny correcting movements to keep the egg rolling straight, it rolls it back into the nest. Even gulls, whose bills are flattened sideways, manage to do this on very uneven ground. If one substitutes a cylindrical object like a tin can for the lost egg and provides a smooth, sloping platform, the bird will bring back the cylinder in the same way, except that the movement will be a smooth sweep, since no corrective motions are needed. Only the moving force —the "propeller"—is needed.

A question that naturally arises when we begin to study the orientation of an an- imal is what sense organ it uses to guide its actions. Clearly, not all sense organs are equally suitable to supply us with cues, or signs, as to where things are—and thus where we are. Our nose may tell us that fresh bread is being baked in a shop some- where near by. But we need our eyes to find it if we want to buy some. This brings out another important point: to be effective in orientation an organ must be sensitive to different degrees of stimulation from dif- ferent directions. It should give information about the distances involved as well.

This kind of sensitivity requires many sensory cells, which are the real receivers

(Text continued on page 82)

A HUMPBACK WHALE leaps through the water during its summer migration north to the Arctic Ocean. The whale'

idance for such long trips may well be a form of "sonar," but how this works in the vast ocean is not known.

of the stimulus; they are connected to the central nervous system by fibers that send messages to the brain. Typical of these marvelous sensory cells are those found in the retina of the eye. Sharpness of eyesight has a direct relationship to visual information about direction; obviously, the sharper its vision, the better an animal can orient itself by visual means. The same applies to hearing. The ears of advanced animals, if used one at a time, are not very good at detecting the direction from which sounds come. But the two ears together give very accurate information. This is because the brain can distinguish minute time differences in the nerve signals coming from the two ears. A sound wave coming from the right reaches the right ear a tiny fraction of a second before it reaches the left one. If the sound is coming from straight ahead, we turn our head to tell whether the source of the sound is in front of us or behind.

Sometimes two different senses, like those of smell and touch, may act together to provide animals with information about where things are. Scent, for instance, is carried by either air or water. Many animals receiving a scent are able to follow it to its source (or, if it spells danger, go away from it) by noting the direction of the wind, if the scent is carried by air, or the current if it is borne by water. Many mammals even use three senses when doing this: their noses alert them to the scent; their sense of touch tells them the direction of the wind that carries the scent (as we might hold up a wet finger); and their eyes guide their final approach.

How do the mechanisms of orientation work? Two things are always involved. First, the animal receives information that it has drifted from the proper position. Next, it acts upon this information until a second sensory message tells it that the required position is regained. This second message provides the "negative feedback," stopping the corrective movement when it has achieved its purpose.

A simple example is that of gravity response, as in a fish that is tilted from its normal position by a sudden current. A tiny weight in each of its inner ears rests on a pad of sensory hairs. In the fish's normal, or horizontal, position the pressure the weight exerts upon the hairs is not felt as a stimulus. But as soon as the fish tilts, the weight bends the hairs to one side. When this occurs, a stimulus is registered. The more the fish tilts, the more the hairs are bent, and the greater the increase in the signals sent to the brain by the nerves attached to the hairs. As the fish brings itself back to normal, the bending of the

Bugging a Sleeping Bear

A grizzly bear, drugged by a sedative, is fitted with a collar so that it can be tracked with electronic equipment. In this way, researchers can learn about the bear's selection of territory, daily and seasonal movements, hibernation and hunting habits, helping them gain insight into how animals orient themselves.

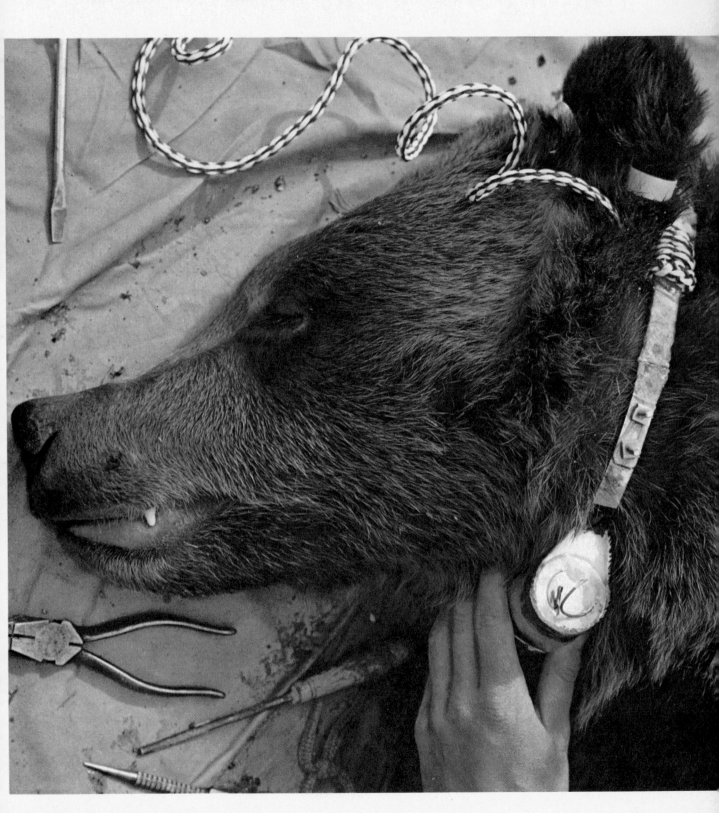

Pronghorn antelopes race from danger, their warnings to their fellows signaled by the flashing patch of white hair on their rumps. In moving, pronghorns are oriented to each other, each going where the herd leads it. This can lead to disaster—herd-oriented animals can be stampeded off cliffs by shrewd hunters.

hairs lessens and the signals are reduced.

In the second phase of the operation, the stimulation from the hairs is transformed into the nervous instructions that govern the movements of the fins and bring the fish upright. Here we encounter a mechanism that we do not yet fully understand and a term that must be explained. The term is "target value." It means simply the aim or purpose of the animal. Thus, for a fish whose desire is to remain quietly "right side up" in the water, the target value is a moderate activity of the sensory nerve stimulated by the balancing mechanism in its ears. This is the only kind of stimulation that does not start the fish making corrective movements; it does nothing, and it stays where it is. If the fish were tipped in the water and its target value were still right side up, then a change in the activity of the nerves would cause a slight correcting movement of the fins to bring the fish back to an upright position.

As complicated as this simple matter of staying right side up may seem to be, other orientation movements present an even greater challenge. Many involve recognizing and acting upon shapes. Our digger wasp offers a good example as it returns to its burrow in the center of a circle of pine cones. What is the image that presents itself as the wasp homes in on the burrow entrance? The entrance has a certain position in the circle. But as the wasp approaches, its own position with respect to the circle is changing all the time. Therefore the image of the circle on the retina of the eye changes too. The wasp must constantly orient itself with respect to a changing image and decreasing distance. Yet it manages to do this and find its way home.

Nor is this the whole story. When the digger wasp has found its burrow and put away its prey, it flies out to hunt more food. What does it orient to now? If it were to base its outward flight on the same stimuli that guide it home, it would automatically return to the burrow as soon as it tried to leave. Quite different stimuli have to be involved to set it on its outward course. This means that the target values have to change. And this change must be governed by the internal state of the animal.

This, in turn, means that the stimulation the animal "expects" when it moves about can be changed by messages from inside the nervous system. One set of values must rule when the wasp is flying to the hunting grounds in search of prey, another when it has found and caught the prey. And this is actually the case, as we know from a brilliant but simple experiment.

The subject of the experiment was a fly. The experiment itself depended on the fly's reaction to things moving in its environment. For an insect that is sitting still and wants to stay that way, the target value might be described as "no movement of the image of the surroundings on the eye," in other words, no apparent motion of the objects around it. This is what the sitting fly is "set" for. Therefore any movement of things around it will start a response. If the fly is resting inside a cylinder whose striped walls slowly begin to turn, the fly will turn too—just enough to keep the stripes where they "belong" and thus satisfy the requirement of "no movement on the retina." This response to movements of the environment is called the "optomotor response."

That is all very well for a fly resting inside a turning cylinder. But what about a fly walking around in a cylinder that is not turning? How does it tell the difference between things that are themselves moving and things that only appear to move because the fly itself is in motion? The usual explanation offered—but never tested—was that the optomotor response was turned off by the fly when it wished to move itself. If it were left on, the reasoning went, the fly would not be able to function. As soon as it turned its head or walked a single step, the various objects around it would also seem to move. The signal from its retina would instantly force it to stop in order to keep the target value of "no movement." Since flies do walk about, it was assumed that the optomotor response must somehow be disconnected when they wished to move.

The men who decided to test this were the German scientists Erich von Holst and Horst Mittelstaedt. They took advantage of the fact that a fly has a very flexible "neck" and can turn its head almost completely around. So they simply twisted a fly's head a full 180° and held it in this unnatural position by gluing it to the fly's body. Now the right eye was on the left side of the fly, and the left on the right, both being upside down. This, in turn, meant that the image on the retinas would move in a direction opposite from the normal whenever the fly turned. Thus, when the fly began to walk and turn, its eyes received a movement stimulus that ran in the opposite direction from the normal.

The question was: how would the fly react to this turned-around life? If the optomotor response, as had always been believed, was shut off when the fly began to walk and turn, the reversed positions of the eyes should not really matter very much. But as the experimenters soon saw, the reversed eye positions mattered a great deal. As the fly began to turn, it got into a mad spin, turning faster and faster in the direction in which it started!

Only one conclusion was possible: the optomotor response was *not* cut off when the fly was walking. Instead a new target value was operating—not "no movement on the retina," which would simply make the fly stop moving, but one that might be labeled "movement at a certain speed and in a certain direction." It was this new target value that the experiment made so clear. If the fly's eyes had been in the right position, it would have been able to move properly. But with their positions reversed, a left turn, for example, was interpreted as a right turn. Attempts to correct this only made the fly turn even farther to the left, or wrong, direction. A mad spin was the only possible result.

Thus it was proved that the brain does manage to "set" the data-processing visual centers in such a way that the target value changes to match the movements an animal intends to make. A normal fly can turn whichever way it wants to. The target values change with it, keeping the turn within the intended bounds. How this is done is a mystery still, but it *is* done.

A simple experiment anyone can perform will illustrate this setting of the target value with respect to movement. If the environment around us moves, we respond to it simply by *seeing* it move. But if we turn our eyes from side to side, we do not have any sensation that the environment is moving, although we know that the image on our retina is moving. This poses the same problem as it does in the fly. Does the target value change from "no movement" to "some movement"? Suppose now that we close one eye and press gently with a finger against the eyelid of the open one. The eyeball will move slightly—but passively, since its movement is caused by the finger and not by its own muscles. What happens? We see the room move.

Why don't we have this same sensation of seeing the room move when we move our eyes spontaneously? When we deliberately move our eyes, our brain is somehow told to expect movement. It is "set" for a

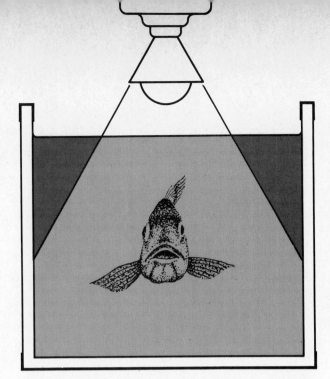

The Sun Is Always "Up"

A fish keeps right side up by orienting itself to the sun and to the pull of gravity. In a small aquarium with a bright light, or "sun," overhead, the fish will stay right side up *(top drawing)*. If the light is put at one side *(center drawing)* the fish will tilt a little, but not much because its balancing organ is still making it react to gravity. But if its balancing organ is removed, the fish will lose its reliance on gravity and flip over on its side *(bottom drawing)* in order to keep the "sun" directly overhead.

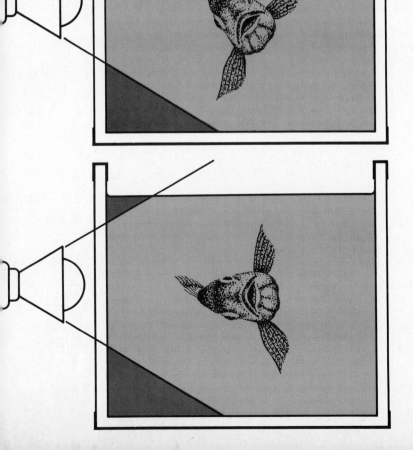

countermovement on the retina. The difference between moving an eye with its own muscles and pushing it around with a finger is that in one case the brain has sent out a command to the eye muscles and in the other it has not. The brain says "move," and so things are "set" to expect movement. If we move the eye with our finger, no command is sent by the brain to the eye muscles through the usual nerve channels. No movement is expected; the target value does not change, and so we see the room move.

Consider the reverse of this situation. Suppose the command "move" is sent to the eyes, but the eyes do not move. This can be done by paralyzing the eye muscles temporarily with an anesthetic. In this case, everything else happens. Movement is expected, a new target value is "set." But the expected visual stimulus does not come because the eyes do not move. The subject sees a movement of the environment even though he cannot turn his eyes—he actually visualizes the target value directly.

Orientation guides almost every link in the behavior chain. With every switch from one act to the next a new orientation mechanism is employed, or "set." When a bee flies from its hive to a flowering plant, it may first respond to a series of landmarks on the way from its hive to the plant. When it comes within sight of the plant, it responds to a rough outline of its shape. We know this because we can mislead the bee by putting up green dummies of roughly the same shape as the plant. When the bee comes nearer, it begins to orient to the colored flowers. When it is still nearer it responds to the "correct" scent, to visual and chemical "honey guides" and to the entrance of the flower. Once the bee has settled on the flower, the scent of the nectar and guiding touch stimuli come into play. All these stimuli start the next stage in the action chain and switch off the preceding act. They also activate the orientation mechanisms and target values.

Target values can also be changed by learning. The homing digger wasp learns new landmarks with each new burrow it digs. The crow returning to the place where it attacked the horned owl the year before does so because it learned this orientation. The salmon returning by scent to the river in which it grew up employs a learned target value. A special and still very puzzling case of a changing target value is the sun navigation of migrant birds. It has been established that starlings migrating southwest in autumn navigate by the sun. In the three hours or so in the morning during which they do their migratory flying, the sun also moves a considerable distance, constantly changing position; yet the starlings keep their course. It has been shown that they change their target value with time; they have an "internal clock." How this internal clock works is still unknown.

A different orientation problem exists wherever a movement of part of the body, such as a limb, is steered by sense organs

Making a Heads-up Dive

When a graylag goose starts a downward dive, its body rolls over in flight, but the head remains upright, as is seen at center below. The goose will then snap its head around and plunge toward earth. The point of this fancy maneuver is to keep the goose from becoming disoriented; if it turned its head with its body, its vision would quickly become topsy-turvy.

not located on that limb, like the eyes. How do you explain a limb movement so fast that the eyes cannot check its performance? The quick stroke of the forelimbs by which a praying mantis grabs a fly is such a movement. When a mantis sees a fly, it turns its head toward it. The rest of the body, including the legs, does not turn. Yet when the mantis strikes, its forelimbs grab the fly almost every time. How do the forelimbs "know" what the eyes have seen—namely the exact direction of the fly with respect to the mantis' body?

Clearly, the limb-aiming mechanism must be informed about the direction and extent of the head movement. This is done by a second sense organ: pads of sensory hairs on the neck are pressed by the head when it turns. It is this, together with the visual information, that tells the nervous system about the direction of the strike. If all the hairs on the sensory pads are shaved off, the mantis will still follow the fly with head movements, but will only be able to strike straight ahead.

An Undercover Test for Rats

Draped with cloth to keep test rats from orienting themselves, a behaviorist runs experiments in a well-wrapped maze. For these tests, three sets of rats were raised in special mazes. One maze had only horizontal passages, another only vertical ones; the third had both. Only the "horizontal" rats, who had never been faced with "upness" or "downness," had trouble getting through the three-dimensional maze.

6

Is Behavior Born or Learned in Animals?

A CAUTIOUS KITTEN peers over the edge of a two-foot drop, which is covered by a sheet of glass the kitten can feel with its paws. Still, the kitten will not step out over the drop. The kitten fears the height even though it has had no previous experience with it. This proves its caution is inborn, not learned.

There is an old catch phrase that says, "animals act instinctively, but man acts intelligently"—meaning that animals are born with a great deal of their adaptive behavior ready-made, whereas man must learn most of his. Of course, we know now that this is not altogether true. There is a great deal more to the story of how behavior develops in the course of an animal's life. This is the general story we shall consider now.

Many animals do not behave efficiently from the start, as a machine does when you turn it on. Nor do animals keep the same behavior patterns throughout their lives. Their behavior machinery changes as they grow up. Sometimes it changes gradually, as a tadpole's wriggling inside the egg develops later into wavy swimming motions for the water, or as a human baby's crawling evolves into walking. But some changes are abrupt and spectacular: a newly hatched butterfly suddenly takes off and flies; a baby chimpanzee suddenly turns a somersault and from then on does it often.

We really know very little about such behavior changes in the course of an animal's development. But we do know enough to

An Instinct
to Move in Circles

Some behavior patterns are so much
a part of an animal at birth that the
animal can never escape their hold.
The caterpillars following each
other endlessly around the rim of a
cup (*right, above*) are trapped by
their rigid instinct to trail after each
other on branches. Similarly, blind
army ants, which instinctively
follow each other's trail by smell
and touch, can be made to march in
an endless circle (*right, below*) by
placing a laboratory dish in their
midst, around which they crawl.
Once started this way, they will
continue marching until they die.

say that the changes are often drastic and of many kinds.

Consider, for example, the many changing activities of a young gull in its first month of life. The chick's first act in entering the world is to push off the egg's "lid" with forceful stretching movements of its neck. The special neck muscle used for this act shrinks after it has done its duty. In the nest, the chick will at first lie quietly, warmed and protected by its parent. In a few hours its downy feathers will dry and become fluffy. But even before it is dry the chick will begin to make weak pecking movements at its parent's beak whenever the parent bends down over the nest. These pecks increase rapidly, and soon the parent will respond by spitting up food. The chick takes up this food and swallows it. During the next hours it will attempt to get up on its legs, and soon it will stand upright.

Now fully in the world, the chick begins to preen its feathers. Before the day is over it will take a few clumsy steps, and at one day old it may even walk out of the nest. When the gull colony is disturbed by an enemy, the parents will fly up and call out the alarm, whereupon the chick will crouch. But when the chick is only a few days older the alarm call will bring on a more complex response: the chick will first run out of the nest, enter cover and then crouch. Soon each chick, when the alarm is sounded, will run to its own hiding place. Within a week the chick will begin to make flying movements. Within two weeks it will begin to call at strangers as its parents do, and soon after it, too, will attack intruders.

Still later, the chick begins to feed by itself. It starts by pecking at many different objects. But after a while it ignores all objects except real food. Meanwhile, its flying movements become stronger, and when the chick is four to five weeks old it can actually fly. But its landings are still very clumsy; at first it will alight without regard for wind direction and force, and it may tumble over two or three times when it lands with a strong tailwind. When it sees water for the first time, it may dip its bill into it and may then drink. At first it will try to drink from any glittering surface, but soon it will recognize water as such. After drinking, it may begin to make bathing movements, but days will pass before it will actually bathe in the water. At first it may even make these movements while standing on land, but facing the water.

This is typical of how behavior develops in many animals. Some movements are performed well, or even perfectly, the first time they are done; they seem to be innate, or born into the animal. Other movements develop gradually, or they are learned. Consider, for example, the way the gull chick crouches the first time the parent gulls fly up in alarm. This looks like "instinctive" behavior, and it may well be. On the other hand, the chick could have heard the alarm call before—while it was still in the egg. It may have associated the alarm with a sensation of chilling, caused by the exposure of the eggs to the air when the parent flew up off them to meet the attacker. Thus crouching could originally have been a response to this chilling, and only later associated directly with the alarm call.

The gradual development of flying movements would seem to be due to the chick's continuous practicing. This has been tested by raising young pigeons in narrow tubes in which there simply was no room to practice flapping. Yet when these "tube birds" were released for the first time, along with other young of the same age who had just learned to fly, the normal way, they flew just as well as the other birds! Obviously the gradual improvement observed under normal conditions can also occur without practice. The clumsy nature of the chick's early attempts may well have been due simply to the fact that the urge to fly was there before the wings and the flying muscles were fully developed.

This goes to show that mere observations, even precise ones, can be misleading. If we want to obtain reliable information as to whether a certain type of behavior is born in the animal or changes through learning —or whether it comes from a combination of the two—we have to experiment.

The first step is to distinguish between causes acting within the animal and those acting on the animal from outside.

Let us consider outside causes first. When a baby goose, or gosling, is hatched from its egg, it is soon able to walk. This walking is directed: it begins to follow its mother. After it has followed the mother for some time, it will not follow anything else. But if we hatch a gosling in an incubator and present it, not with its mother, but with another animal or even an object like a blue balloon, it will follow this abnormal object. And once it has followed the balloon for some time, it will continue to do so and refuse to follow a real mother goose. As students of behavior say, the gosling has become "imprinted" on the artificial parent—on whatever first started its response to follow.

This shows that in order to behave normally—that is, to follow its mother—the gosling had to be exposed to the mother first. To use a term associated with computers, the gosling had not been completely "programmed" for its following response. Whatever the gosling might have had in the way of an innate response had to be added to by exposure to the outside world.

In other cases no such extra "programming" is required: the response is clearly not learned. If we hatch a black-headed gull chick in an incubator, keep it in complete darkness for a few hours and then show it models of the parent's bill, we find that it responds more vigorously to red models—the natural color of the adult's bill—than to those of any other color. Since the chick had never seen an adult gull, its programming with respect to bill color must have been internal.

From these examples, it is clear that behavior machinery can be programmed either from within or from without. The external programming is done through adjustments made as a result of the animal's experience with the outside world. The internal programming is the result of the slow evolution of the animal itself. It was achieved through a long trial-and-error process; through generation after generation this process got rid of animals unable to cope with their environment. It preserved the well-programmed types, those who could make the adjustments needed to survive.

The way an animal's behavior is programmed, or learned, was made famous by the experiments of the Russian scientist Ivan Pavlov. Pavlov taught animals to respond to a stimulus, which, before he started, meant nothing to them. He would, for example, ring a bell every time he gave a dog some food. After many such experiences, the dog would drool in anticipation of food every time a bell was rung. The point is that the dog does not normally drool at the ringing of a bell, but it can be taught to do so. In this case, the dog's behavior was programmed into it through repeated experience in the laboratory. But the same kind of learning process occurs repeatedly in nature. Birds of prey return regularly to places where they have hunted successfully. My cat reacts the same way; it runs to the kitchen when it hears me sharpening the carving knife. Experience has taught it that food is on the way.

Living by Hanging Upside Down

The very survival of the eyed hawk moth caterpillar depends on an inborn behavioral act. The coloring of the caterpillar is such that when it hangs from the underside of a twig *(above)*, the light coming from overhead gives it a uniform shade and makes it hard for hungry birds to see. But if turned over *(below)*, the caterpillar immediately becomes visible. If put in this position, it hurries to get back under the twig, since its normal behavior is to remain upside down.

Learning by copying, though rare among animals, is a form of interacting with the environment. Something like it is found in some songbirds that learn to sing properly only by listening to others of their species. If young chaffinches are raised without hearing other chaffinches sing, they do not develop their normal song. All they produce is a kind of warble. But if, in the early weeks of their lives, they can hear the song of experienced males, they develop the normal song of the species. Some species of birds possess this gift of copying a song to a high degree; the world champion is probably the myna bird of Southeast Asia, which can actually imitate the songs of other birds and even the speech of man.

A German friend of mine performed an amusing experiment on this subject, using bullfinches. He had one young male bullfinch chick raised by a female canary. The bullfinch, surrounded by other canaries, learned their song, copying it so exactly that its song could not be told from that of a true canary. Later this bullfinch mated with a female of its own species and the pair raised young together. Two males of this brood learned the canary song from their father and sang it perfectly when they were grown up. One of these was sent to a bird specialist two miles away and mated there with a female bullfinch. Two years later, one of the sons of this pair, a grandson of the original male, was returned to my friend. It rewarded him by singing like a canary too—the song its grandfather had learned four years before!

All these examples of learning have two

UNFAMILIAR

BECOMING FAMILIAR

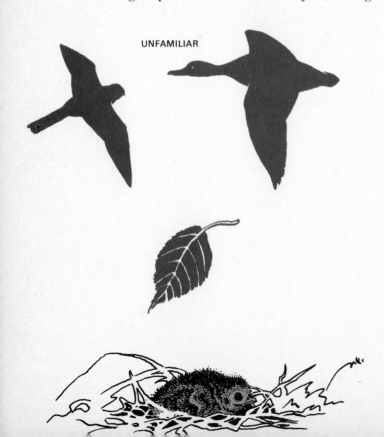

things in common: the behavior is not perfect the first time it appears, and to improve it the animal must gain experience.

The most complex learning probably occurs in monkeys and apes, and in man. Harry F. Harlow and his co-workers at the University of Wisconsin have carried out fascinating studies of behavior development in rhesus monkeys. While the innate equipment of most lower animals is relatively complete from the start, that of Harlow's monkeys turned out to be only a set of vague, general urges and needs, which have to be developed by constant interplay with the environment. Basic among these needs is the need for security. A normal rhesus mother gives its young security by allowing the baby to cling to its body. Infants denied this and other expressions of motherly

care are too frightened to venture out on any explorations; thus they fail to learn from the vital experience of the outside world. The same lack of motherly care has had effects on the infants' later social life. They fail to develop close bonds with their companions. They do not even mate normally, becoming either very aggressive or indifferent. Similar results have been observed in other mammals such as cats, rats and goats. There can be little doubt that many of these findings also apply to human infants. Mankind, in fact, relies even more heavily on experience.

In most animals, however, much of the programming of the behavior machinery is not done externally, but internally. Experiments to learn more about how this actually happens have not yet been performed on

STILL UNFAMILIAR

A Fear of Unfamiliar Shapes

The chicks of many fowl crouch in alarm when a short-necked hawk passes overhead, but ignore harmless, long-necked birds like ducks. Because of this, behaviorists concluded the chicks had an inborn ability to tell hawks from other birds. But this is not true. When chicks are first born, they crouch when anything passes overhead, even a falling leaf (*far left*). As they grow older, they get used to such common objects and lose their fear of them (*middle*). The chicks, however, still crouch when hunting birds such as hawks fly by (*left*)—because these birds appear so seldom that their shapes are unfamiliar.

A Case of Growing Up

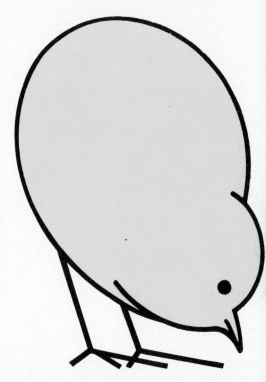

CHICK WITHOUT PRISMS

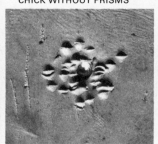

An interesting experiment has proved that a chick's pecking ability, which improves as the chick grows older, is the result of growing up, not of any learning process. In this test, a seed was set in soft clay. At first, the pecks of a chick with normal eyesight were scattered around the seed (*above, left*). But after three days, the peck marks were closer to the seed (*above, right*). The same test was tried with a

CHICK WITH PRISMS

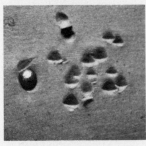

chick fitted with goggles (*see photograph*), which contained prisms that deflected its vision to one side. At first its peck marks were in a loose pattern and all to the right of the seed (*above, left*). After three days, the peck marks were closer together, but still to the right of the food (*above, right*). If the chick had "learned" to peck closer patterns, it would have "learned" to adjust to the deflected vision caused by the goggles.

any large scale. But one example is worth mentioning in detail.

If we tickle the skin on the back of a frog, the frog will respond by scratching the tickled spot with a well-aimed movement of its leg. Tickle its belly, and the frog will scratch its belly. This is possible because sensory nerves running from each part of the skin to the spinal cord provide the frog with information about the spot where it was stimulated.

Now, let us step in at a very early state of development before the nerves growing out from the frog's spinal cord have actually made contact with the skin. If we exchange a bit of the frog's back skin with a bit of belly skin, we will see something surprising. After the nerves have had time to make connection between the skin and the spinal cord, this particular frog, if tickled on the back, will scratch its belly—and vice versa!

This fascinating experiment allows only one explanation, and a very startling one at that. To begin with, the two patches of skin developed normally even though they had been transplanted. The piece of back skin grew dark green although it was on the white belly, and the piece of belly skin grew white even though it was on the dark green back. This proved that there were chemical differences in the two patches from the beginning. These chemical differences apparently made themselves known to the nerves. In effect they said, "I am a piece of back skin" or "I am a piece of belly

101

skin," no matter where they were located. In short, the function of the nerve, unsure at first, was settled once and for all by the chemical nature of the bit of skin into which it had grown, and not by the location of that bit of skin.

Here, then, is a clear-cut indication of a kind of internal programming, for the skin programs its sensory nerves. How this takes place is still unknown, but the evidence that it does happen is clear.

So far, we know almost nothing about the internal control of the development of behavior. And we still know far too little about how it is affected by external experience.

But we have learned a few things. We know, for instance, that many complex behavior patterns are neither all internal nor all external but a combination of the two. This is shown by the way squirrels crack hazelnuts. A hazelnut has a groove in its shell. An experienced squirrel will grasp the nut in such a way that it can gnaw at this groove, quickly deepening it. Then it will turn the nut in its front paws, give it a hard bite and the nut will crack open.

This efficient procedure contrasts strongly with that of a young squirrel raised on other kinds of food and with no chance to practice handling, gnawing and cracking.

Learning What to Eat

The diet of some creatures is instinctive: they eat certain things automatically from birth. But often tastes for food are learned through experience. The pictures at the right show how a southern toad learns what is good to eat and what is not. This toad's normal diet consists of insects, and its instinct is to snap up anything that wiggles like one. Up to the time these pictures were taken, this particular toad had never seen either a bumblebee or a robber fly —an insect that looks like a bee but cannot sting. Out of this experience came a useful lesson: the toad learned to avoid bees.

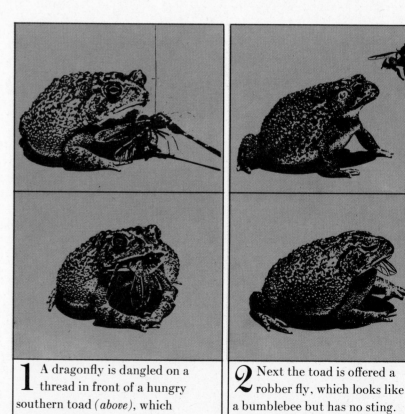

1 A dragonfly is dangled on a thread in front of a hungry southern toad (*above*), which quickly gobbles it up (*below*).

2 Next the toad is offered a robber fly, which looks like a bumblebee but has no sting. The toad happily swallows it.

True, this inexperienced squirrel will start in as if it were the most skillful nutcracker. It will grasp the nut, turning it over and over and chewing at it with great energy; after a time, it will try to crack the nut open. However, all these efforts are useless. Instead of holding the nut so that it can gnaw at the groove, it gnaws all over the surface. As a result its cracking efforts are in vain, and it has to start over again. In short, the squirrel is programmed internally for handling, for gnawing and for cracking. But it must learn by experience how to do these things well.

An animal's ability to learn changes during the course of its life. Many things are learned only at certain times. A duckling or a gosling, for example, cannot be "imprinted" with its mother's particular image at just any time. The ability to learn what its mother looks like and follow her appears soon after hatching, reaches a peak in a few hours and then gradually wanes. If a duckling is hatched alone in an incubator and is kept locked up for a few days, it will lose the ability to become imprinted.

Differences in learning ability and general intelligence occur throughout the animal kingdom. Apes are more intelligent than

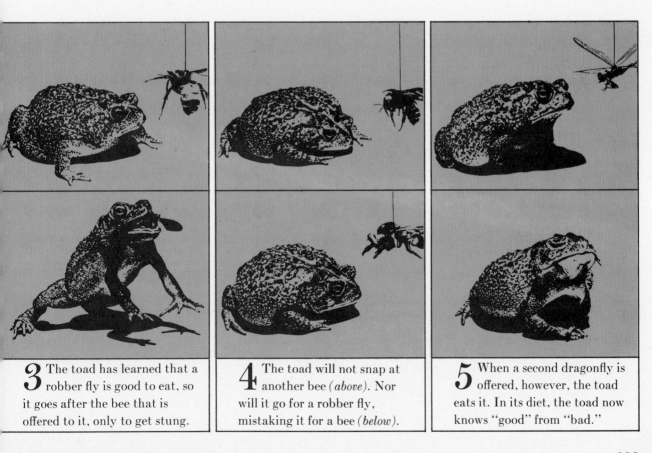

3 The toad has learned that a robber fly is good to eat, so it goes after the bee that is offered to it, only to get stung.

4 The toad will not snap at another bee (*above*). Nor will it go for a robber fly, mistaking it for a bee (*below*).

5 When a second dragonfly is offered, however, the toad eats it. In its diet, the toad now knows "good" from "bad."

rabbits; crows, parrots and geese are more intelligent than hawks, gulls or chickens. But there are equally deep differences that do not depend on intelligence. A murre, a kind of northern sea-bird, is no more intelligent than a gull, and yet it always learns to recognize its own eggs, which gulls do not. Gulls are smart enough to do this, and their eggs are different enough to permit it. Why, then, do they not do so? The answer is that they have another way of locating their nests—by learning the landmarks around them. Provided it is in the right place, a gull will accept as its own anything that looks like an egg, even a potato. Murres, on the other hand, have to learn to recognize their own eggs because they do not build nests, and their eggs may roll

A Reasoning Rat and His Ladder Trick

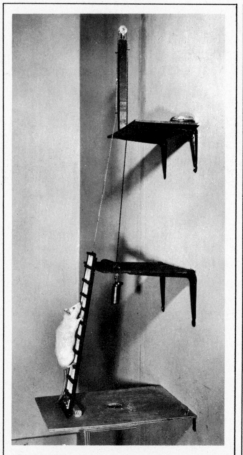

1 A white rat used in a test combines inborn ability with experience to get at a piece of cheese. Above, it smells the cheese but sees no way to reach it.

2 Finding the ladder, the rat scampers up. The ladder is attached to a chain with a counter-weight looped over a pulley on the top shelf.

3 The rat, which has been specially bred and trained for tests such as these, pulls on the chain, raising the ladder toward the middle platform.

about on the rock ledges. Thus each species develops its behavior in a way that seems best suited to its needs.

Both an animal's behavior and the way it develops are remarkably efficient. It is clearly of great advantage to a bird to be able to fly well the first time it tries. The presence of many enemies makes this a must—it is simply too dangerous to have to learn flying clumsily and slowly the way we learn to walk or swim. On the other hand, it would be a handicap to a bird if its innate knowledge of what was acceptable food were too specialized. By trying out a variety of things and learning by experience to eat food that is good for it and that is at the same time plentiful, a particular species will manage to make the most of different habi-

The rat stops pulling and peers over the edge to see how the ladder doing. It will then tug the chain til the ladder reaches the shelf.

5 By pulling some more, the rat gets the ladder up on the middle shelf. Then the rat climbs the rest of the way toward its final goal, the piece of cheese.

6 Victorious at last, the rat eats the cheese. The test shows that unless the rat had inborn reason, it could not have reached the cheese.

tats and different seasons of the year.

What about our own species? How does man fit into this picture? Of course we know that we learn a great deal, but do we also have a basic, internally programmed set of behaviors? This is extremely difficult to decide, for we do not like to carry out experiments on our fellow humans—certainly not the kind of drastic experiments that would be required. For example, we would not allow anybody to raise a human baby in isolation, as we do animals in tests. So we have to rely on indirect evidence.

Man seems to have simple inborn reactions to simple stimuli—motor patterns like eye blinking, yawning, weeping and smiling, the basic pattern of walking and such simple responses as the flicking movements by which we brush an insect off our skin. In addition, we probably have some kind of internal programming at higher levels. An example is the responsiveness in men to certain complex stimuli supplied by women, and vice versa. We should also mention aggressive behavior and motherly nursing behavior patterns.

To what extent can we control man's aggressiveness through educational measures, for example? To what extent can we control man's willingness to be taught? What about the very techniques of teaching? With questions like these unanswered it is not surprising that the development of behavior is being studied carefully in our nearest relatives, the monkeys and apes.

Much of the adult social behavior of monkeys and apes, as well as other higher animals, is deeply influenced by the relations the animals had with their mothers when they were young. Normal motherly love is necessary for the development of many kinds of social behavior later in life. Observation of human beings shows that this is true of our species as well.

But observation can never be as convincing as experiments, and since we cannot perform extensive experiments on our fellow humans much of our understanding of the development of human behavior will have to come from the study of animals. In the end, this application of our work to the understanding of man may be the most important reason for animal behavior studies —even though it is a selfish one.

Learning to Live with Man

A little European bird called the great tit has a habit of shredding papery bark from trees. With the arrival of civilization it has neatly turned this innate talent to the tops of milk bottles as well. Here the bird pecks a hole in the foil wrapping of a bottle left on a doorstep and drinks the cream at the top.

7

Living Together in Order to Survive

Some of man's deepest human experiences, and many of his highest achievements, are due to his social nature, his urge to do things and share experiences and ideas with other men. At the same time, man's social attitudes include hostility, intolerance and hatred. As his population has increased and his control over his environment has grown, these baser characteristics have become more and more dangerous until, today, they threaten mankind with self-destruction. Even if we were not interested in the social behavior of animals for its own sake, our longing for happiness, our mere hope for survival should encourage us to take a close look at the ways in which our social fellow animals deal with the very real problems of living together.

Most animals are, at one time or another, "social." It is not hard to appreciate the so-

SPACED LIKE SOLDIERS, South Atlantic king penguins hatch their eggs, keeping about a flipper's length apart. Each female penguin produces one egg, which it balances on its feet and warms with its stomach. This type of regimented behavior is typical of animals living clustered in communities.

cial nature of herds of African big game, of schools of fish, of flocks of migrating birds, of societies of termites. But the way animals treat one another, the way they "interact," is often hard to call "social." The interaction between parents and offspring, for example, is sometimes harsh. The fighting between rival males in spring might even seem to be antisocial. Yet all these interactions have a great deal in common. All contribute to the success of the species and all depend on communication between individuals. The methods used by different animals to achieve this communication are basically the same.

The simplest kind of social behavior is herding, schooling or flocking—just being together. Yet we must not consider all gatherings of animals to be social. The insects that whirl together around a lamp on a summer night may have been attracted separately to the light, and may interact no more than snowflakes falling to the ground. For groups to be called social, the animals must at least remain with each other as they move from place to place. Something holds bees in a swarm, starlings in a flock and wildebeests in a herd.

However, social animals do much more than merely stay together. They *do* things together. A family of ducklings in the park does the same things at the same time. Part of the day they all feed, keeping close together wherever they go. At other times they bathe together, and after a bath they swim to shore together and spend half an hour or so preening, standing next to each other. Then they fall asleep, side by side.

Some animals go still further in their social behavior. Members of a group may divide up the work to be done. This division of labor is seen in its most marked form in the social insects. In a beehive, there is a queen, there are thousands of workers and at certain times of the year there are males or drones. Each of these groups has its own part in the life of the hive. Even the jobs of the workers are divided up; depending on their age, they will feed the brood, or do the outside food hunting, or stand guard and drive away strangers, or even keep the hive from getting too hot or too cold.

There is also a division of labor in more solitary animals: the sharing of tasks between male and female. In the higher animals this applies not only to the different roles in mating but also to the task of looking after the young. For instance, the male and female jewelfish take turns guarding and guiding their offspring. In a flock of geese, which has no single leader, all the geese, and particularly the adult males, take their turn on guard duty. Among baboons the young males tend to stray from the main group and so are apt to spot an enemy first; in chimpanzees the old, experienced males lead the group and keep a sharp lookout at all times.

In short, social behavior depends on various types of interactions among individuals, each playing its part in communicating with others. If we are to understand this fully, we must ask the same question about social interaction that we asked about the behavior of an individual animal. How does social behavior benefit a race of animals? How is it organized? How do social systems develop? And how have they evolved?

Social interactions may be helpful in many and often obvious ways. Most kinds of animal could not exist without cooperation between male and female for the purpose of mating. And species in which the young receive parental care need close cooperation between parents and young. Living in crowded conditions may have various advantages too. Social caterpillars keep each other warm and so speed up each others' development. As we have seen, the gulls of a breeding colony attack enemies in force, and this united defense is much more successful than individual attacks on the enemy. This success is possible because the gulls nest close together and at exactly the same time of year.

Since social living offers so many advantages, one might well ask why there are lone or solitary animals at all. The answer is that being alone can also be useful, though in different ways. For instance, most animals whose pattern or color blends with their surroundings, like caterpillars or frogs, live scattered. This is because many predatory animals can find even the most skillfully camouflaged prey if they really turn their attention to it. This they do only when they can find enough of these animals to make the hunt worthwhile.

Animals are able to live alone in many different ways. The most efficient way to insure a relatively solitary life is by fighting. That is one of the reasons why so many animals fight regularly. Even social animals keep each other at a certain distance. They set a limit to their crowding. Starlings, crows and gulls often fight over food. Many higher animals, at least in the reproductive season, defend their own "territory." In such species it is usually the males that drive off rival males from their chosen piece of ground. Thus even a "solitary" animal interacts with others at times and from this point of view must also be called social.

In all these examples it is easy to see that the aggressor benefits when he wins. But in almost every fight, there must also be a loser; what advantage can there be in losing? The answer is that aggression pays only if you win, and if you face a superior opponent it is wiser to withdraw. Success goes to the animal that knows when to run as well as when to attack. Thus survival value is based on knowing when to attack and when to run rather than simply on blind aggressiveness.

The many advantages of social interaction have led to the evolution of many different types of community life in the animal world. And in social life something new is added—communication. When animals communicate with each other through

GRAYLAG GOOSE—AT EASE

"Talking" with Postures

Community-dwelling animals in particular have special ways of communicating with each other. To humans, speech is considered the best way to communicate, but we often forget how expressive our smiles, tears, body postures and hand gestures can be. A man, if he has to, can get along without talking. Similarly, many animals can "speak" to one another without uttering a sound. The graylag goose does this by holding its body in certain positions. The goose uses its "voice" to call in anger, but generally it indicates its feelings by postures like those shown here.

their actions, they are "talking." This "language" has been studied in many species. Compared with human speech it is very simple, but whereas our language is based mainly on sounds, animal communication is more varied and richer because many of the other senses can be involved. In fact, any sense organ can be used for signaling by animals.

We are only beginning to discover how many animals communicate with chemicals. A simple example is found among barnacles. These small sea animals start life as free-floating larvae carried at will by the sea currents. Only when they grow older do they adopt a fixed life, dropping to the bottom, growing shells and anchoring themselves to rocks or pilings or the bottom of boats. They prefer to spend their fixed stage on or near old barnacle beds—which is why we almost always find barnacles in clumps. And they locate existing beds by the "barnacle scent" given off by adult barnacles.

The sense of touch is also used by many animals for receiving signals. After a female

THREATENING AT A DISTANCE   ALL-OUT ATTACK

stickleback has been brought into the nest by the male, she cannot spawn until the male stimulates her by touching the base of her tail; when we prevent a male from touching her she will not spawn.

Since we ourselves communicate mainly by sounds and visual signals, it is not surprising that these are the types of language that we have studied most among animals. Many locusts, frogs, a few reptiles and almost all birds use a variety of sounds as signals. A regular, simple sound, repeated at intervals, is used by many social birds to keep the flock together.

Of all the signals used by animals, it is the visual ones that have been studied the most. They include movements, postures and the type of signal that we ourselves use in such things as flags, traffic lights and navigation beacons. For instance, in many birds the males are much more brightly colored than the females. While the females need camouflage as part of the protection of their brood from birds of prey,

APPROACH TO A MATE

POSTURE OF INFERIORITY

CONFLICT: AGGRESSION AND FEAR

DEFENSIVE POSTURE

113

the males can risk showing these bright colors. And they use them in a variety of ways in courtship and in the vital business of driving away rivals. The movements they make when courting and threatening are always well adapted to showing off the bright colors. Sometimes a male seems like just one large flag. In species that use camouflage, the bright colors are more often kept hidden and are shown only when they are needed. In these cases effective signaling by color depends on behavior as well. The European robin, for instance, is perfectly camouflaged on the back, but a male in the fighting mood puffs up its brick-red breast and presents this warning signal to other males trying to invade its territory.

What is the nature of all these signals? What kinds of messages do they convey? This we can find out only through study of the way animals respond to them. As a rule the message is very simple. In many cases a signal does no more than any other external stimulus; it sets off an immediate response. One alarm call given by a gull makes all its neighbors look around. A mating call makes a female move toward the male. A hostile posture drives away a rival. The red patch on the bill tip of a parent herring gull makes the chick peck at it and so reach the food presented.

Are there any useful lessons in all this for man? It is, of course, very important to know how much social environment can

(*Text continued on page 118*)

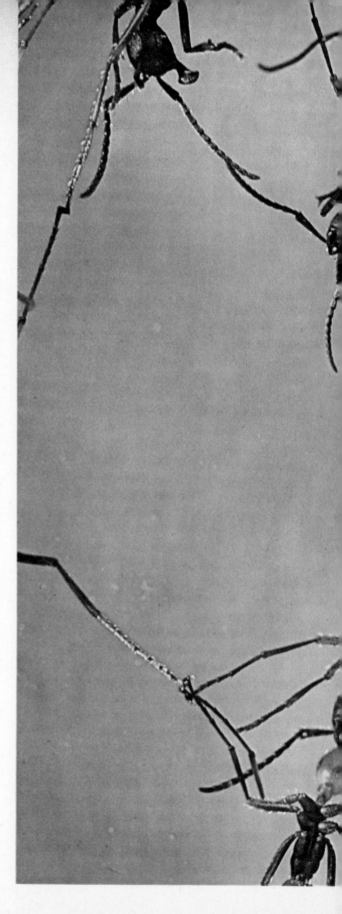

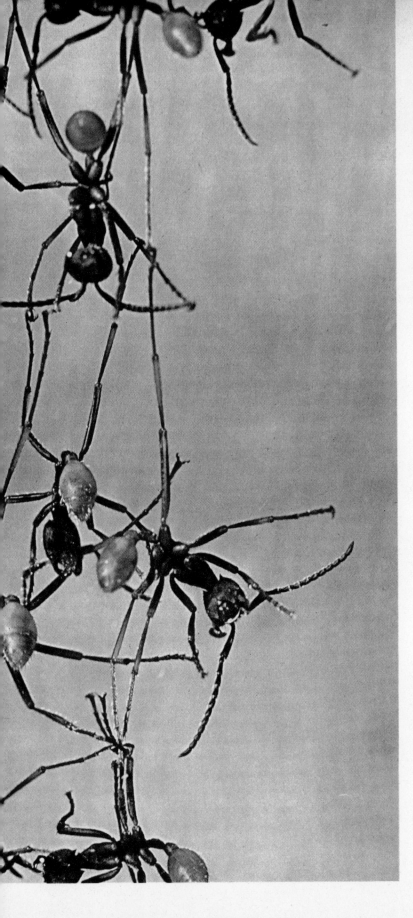

A Living Defense

The blind, meat-eating army ant of the tropical forests lives in colonies, which when they march kill and devour practically everything in their path. The ants move by night and camp by day, working together in specialized jobs. At left, acrobatic worker ants interlock legs to form part of a living network of defenses around their queen and its brood.

A Society in the Dunes

A community of black-headed gulls may look like a scene of mass confusion, but it is actually a well-organized society. Since single nests may be raided by such enemies as crows (*1, key at left*), the nests are grouped for mutual defense (*7*). Even neighboring gulls may sometimes try to eat the eggs

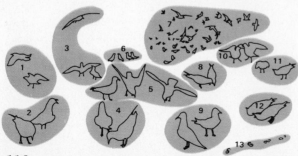

or young, so the male warns them off (2). Protective coloration also helps hide eggs and chicks from prowling foxes, whose tracks are seen in the sand (13).

The gulls' mating ritual begins in the spring, when their white face feathers turn dark, giving them fierce, threatening masks. An urge to stake out its own territory rises in each male, sometimes ending in a fight (10). More often the males may spread their wings and bob angrily (5), or give warning calls at other males on the ground (6) or in the air (3). These calls also attract unmated females. At first, males and females are hostile and suspicious (11), but then they reduce the threat, standing parallel and raising their bills (12) or turning away (9). In a while, the male spits up food for the female to eat (8), then lures her to the nesting site by bobbing his head over it (4).

A Changing of the Guard

For protection, many fishes, like the jewelfish (*above*), keep their young in schools, which they lead in a zigzag course. When the parents relieve each other, they have a special way of changing the guard. One parent comes in rapidly, in a straight line, then starts zigzagging to attract the attention of the school (*left*). Instantly, the other parent darts away in a straight line, and the school is undisturbed.

mold social responses. Human beings, let us face it, are very aggressive. We have developed the means of blowing up the world and ourselves without developing efficient ways of keeping ourselves in check. And this brings us to the question: What can animal behavior teach us about ourselves?

It is not known at the moment whether or not our aggressiveness is born in us, or whether educational methods could be found to produce non-aggressive men. Here we can learn a great deal from the study of animals. We can investigate how education could avoid increasing aggressiveness, as it may well be doing today in competitive societies. We can teach sensitivity and imagination and compassion for the victims of aggression; this is urgent because our long-range weapons allow us to kill and wound at a distance where the cries and signs of suffering of our fellow men cannot be seen or heard. We can try to discover the best ways to find an outlet for aggression—by finding symbolic sticks to attack, tables to bang or, better yet, by conquering nature as in the exploration of space or in some gigantic power or irrigation project. In these and other ways the study of the social behavior of animals may well help us to serve —and very possibly to save—ourselves, and thus it may emerge as the most important science of all.

Animal behavior studies concerning aggression, community life and communication lead us to think of the ways animals survive. Animal behavior shows an almost endless variety of ways to survive. The basic machinery of behavior, made up of sensory, nerve, muscle and gland cells, determines what an animal does. Each arrangement of this machinery is unique for each species of animal, and each efficiently meets the demand of a hostile world in its own way. We must now try to discover how this efficiency has come about.

As we know, the many animal types that live on the earth today are the result of a long process of evolution. To understand how this evolution came about is one of the major tasks of biology. In many cases, we can learn how animals evolved physically by studying fossils, the imprints of their skeletons left in clay that has turned to rock. But how did their behavior evolve? Fossils cannot tell us whether or not ancient animals acted differently from their modern-day descendants. But through experiments and guesses, we can form some ideas.

As we have said before, the animals best equipped to survive outlive and outbreed those not as well equipped. This process is called evolution by natural selection. It no doubt applies to an animal's behavior too. If natural selection has been responsible for the evolution of the behavior in an animal, then the way an animal is behaving right now must help its species survive.

The first step is to find out whether a given behavior helps an animal adjust to the dangers of its environment. For example, we know that a bird needs the heat insulation provided by the air caught in its feathers. And the bird responds to cold weather by fluffing its plumage and so enlarging the air layer. Thus we can be sure that plumage fluffing is useful as a protection against the cold. In another case, experiments have shown that insect-eating birds find a caterpillar more easily when the caterpillar is sitting in the "wrong" position, that is, in a position that does not help it blend into the foliage. This proves that the posture of the caterpillars is part of their defense against birds.

These, and scores of other examples, show that behavior has indeed evolved. It has evolved to help the animal meet the many pressures and dangers of its surroundings.

But if behavior has evolved to help the animal survive, why are there so many cases of behavior that seem to fail the animal? A colony of black-headed gulls would seem to have perfect defenses against invasions by enemies like crows. Yet crows do break through these defenses. This hints that the gull's defenses could be better. But a closer study of the problem shows that an improvement in one way would be harmful in another. Crows are dangerous to adult gulls as well as to their eggs. If the adult were too aggressive toward an enemy crow, it might be attacked and killed. In sum, it is overall efficiency in surviving that is promoted by the evolution of behavior. It must lead to compromise solutions. For example, a goose's foot is not very good for either

swimming or walking, but it does both reasonably well. Although the empty eggshell on the rim of a gull's nest endangers the brood because it is easily seen, it is not removed promptly. This may seem less than perfect—but as long as a chick is still wet it is without defenses. The parent gull cannot take the shell away from the nest without leaving the chick alone and exposed. So the parent usually compromises by leaving the shell where it is until the chick has dried.

No animal has a perfect defense against its enemies. As the animal improves its defenses, the enemy steps up the efficiency of its attack. A shrimp hides itself well by digging into the sand, but a cuttlefish can crack its defenses by its trick of blowing the sand away. Man has created many changes in the environment of animals that evolution, slow as it is, has not yet been able to cope with. For instance, the wholesale drainage of marshes in Western Europe has forced the black-headed gull to move to sand dunes, which are not as good as a breeding habitat. For one thing, the gulls sometimes suffer heavy losses from foxes,

(Text continued on page 124)

Family Life in a Paper Home

Paper wasps carry on their community life in shelters made of pulp formed into six-sided cells *(left)*. The dots at center are the eggs; the larvae are in units nearby, and the closed cells at far left hold the developing pupae. Adults feed their offspring, which, in turn, give off a sugary saliva that the wasps eat.

121

A Busy, Underground "Town"

A prairie dog community is organized like a busy, well-run little town. The basic social group is usually two males, two females, a few youngsters and several babies. Each group defends its territory against its neighbors; the group's members recognize each other by sight, but they often make sure by exchanging "kisses" *(1)*, *(2)*. From time to time they

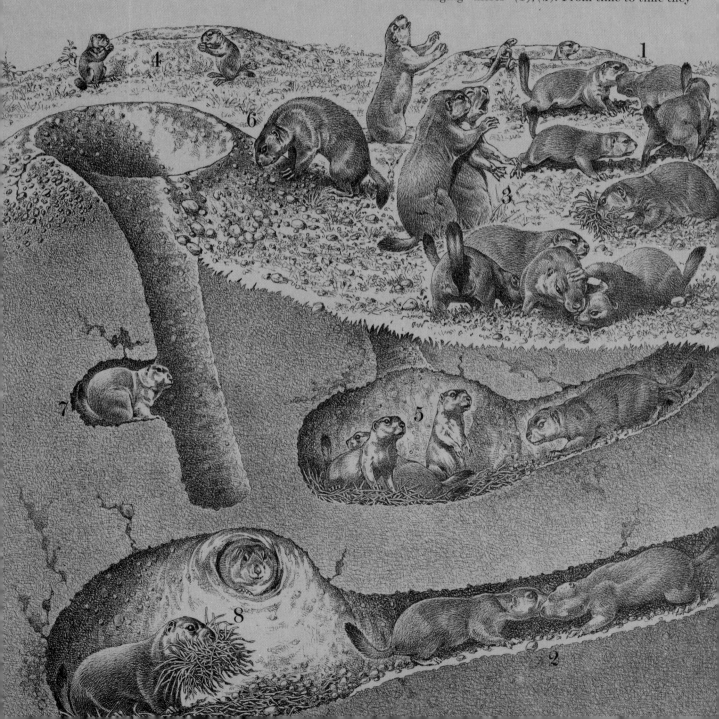

also help groom each other (3). Prairie dogs feed only during the day (4), living on grasses, roots and seeds; they bring this food to the babies, which stay in the nest (5). The design of the tunnels is always the same. Earth is piled around the entrance (6) as a dike against flash floods. A guard room (7) makes a handy retreat when an animal is threatened.

The nest (8), lined with grass, is at the rear. Empty tunnels may be occupied by burrowing owls (9) and diamond-back rattlesnakes (10), neither of which is a threat to the dogs. However, the badger (11) and the black-footed ferret (12) are deadly enemies—more so than the coyote (13), which cannot get down in the holes.

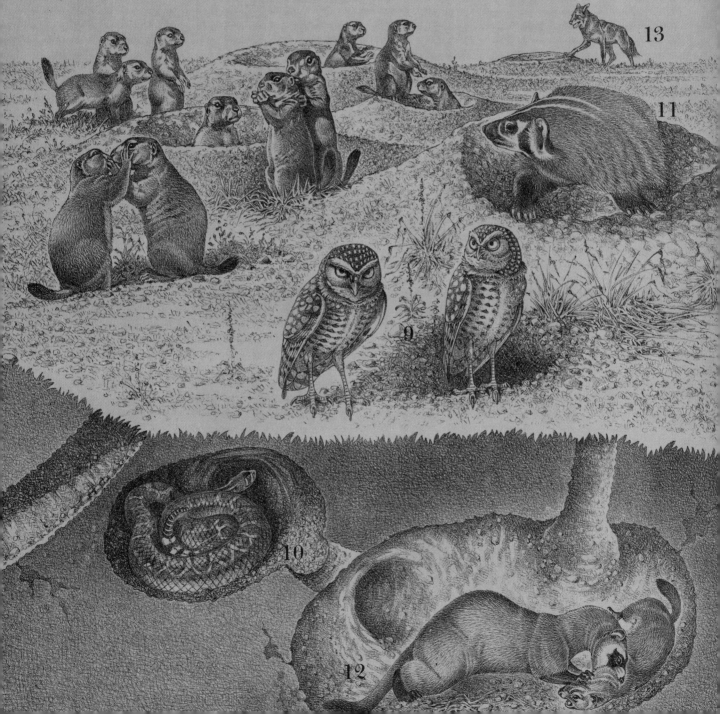

which in the dunes are not handicapped by water as they would be in a marsh.

How does man fit into this picture? At first glance, we might seem unique. But we know from fossils that our species not too long ago evolved from ape-like animal forms. Therefore, our special characteristics must have evolved from animal beginnings. And indeed we are beginning to recognize in animals many clues to human behavior.

Man may seem unique in his ability to learn—but many animals learn extremely well. Man's ability to look into the future, to think of the future effects of his actions, is much more highly developed than that of any animal. But, as we have seen, animals do show primitive signs of being aware of the future. Our powers of thinking—reasoning, forming ideas and understanding cause and effect—may well have grown out of abilities that we see in animals. Again, social animals have crude elements of some of our "moral" standards; animal parents care for their young and show respect for a leader. But we do not really understand these things well, because so far we have hardly applied the same methods of study to ourselves that we are applying to animals. It is astonishing but true that we do not even have good knowledge, based on scientific observation, of the most common behavior patterns of human infants, let alone adults.

The evolution of human society and behavior in the last 10,000 years or so has progressed much more rapidly than in any other animal. Most of our change has not been physical. In fact our bodies have changed very little since Cro-Magnon man first appeared. Most of our change is the product of handing on learned knowledge. New habits spread in a similar way among animals too, on a different scale. But for us this handing on of learned knowledge has had one dangerous consequence: we have changed and rebuilt our own environment, including our social environment, so fast that it has outpaced our natural behavior patterns. We cannot hope to speed up behavioral evolution to cope with these terrifying changes. Our only hope lies in adjusting ourselves by learning to cope with our new and rapidly changing environment. This is why the study of man's behavior is a task of the greatest urgency.

A Special Relationship

Most animals have learned to live together in one way or another, some species evolving complex societies for survival, others going it largely alone. The mixed trio at right has worked out its own very special relationship, the little girl conveying in her touch its simple basis: dependence, protection and love.

Index

Numerals in italics indicate a photograph
or painting of the subject mentioned.

Action chains, 58-65
Adaptive behavior, 8-16; in black-headed gull, 11-13; in cuttlefish, 13-15; in stickleback, 9-10; in yucca moth, 9
Aggressiveness, by female ostrich, *72-73*
Anhinga (bird), *58-59*
Animal behavior: "conflict behavior," *66-67*, 68-71; definition of, 8; efficiency of, 105-106; environment as control of, 57-60; hormones as control of, 57-60, *70-71;* importance of timing to, 19; imprinting of, 96; inborn, *92*, *94*, 95-96, *97*, 99-102, *104-105;* instinctive, 93, 95, 96; learning process of young gull, 95; lessons to be learned from, 114-118, 124; "mixed" behavior generally impossible, 68; must be controlled in space, 75-90; partly result of experience, 93-105; programmed both internally and externally, 96-97, 99-103; research needed to determine, 20-26; as result of muscle activity, 15; social existence, 109-124; and the unexpected, 16; understanding it, 5
Animals, conditioning of, *14-15*, *22*, *23*, 28-29, 57-58, 97
Antelope, pronghorn, *85*
Ants: army, defensive formation of, *114-115;* army, instinct to follow, *94;* learning ability of, *11*
Appetitive behavior, 60

Baboons, *32;* defensive stance of, *64-65;* division of labor among, 110
Baby features, appeal of, *38-39*
Balance, in fish, 87
Barnacles, 112
Bats: hearing of, 30-31, *74;* sounds by, 30-31
Bear, grizzly, electronic tracking of, *83*
Bees: color vision of, 10, 20, 23, *31*, 35-36; direction-giving dance of, *12-13;* orientation by, 88; potential food for toad, *102-103;* as prey of digger wasp, 61-*62-63;* and red and blue light, 23, 36; social behavior of, 110; and ultraviolet light, 20, 23-25, 30, *31*
Beetles: water (*Dytiscus marginalis*), 41-44, 46; whirligig, *29*
Behavior chains, *34*, *58-59*, 63-72; guided by orientation, 88; why they stop, 65-71
Birds: color differentiation between sexes, 113-114; "conflict behavior" in, 71; copying of songs by, 98; feeding behavior of baby, *36-37;* reaction to cold by, 119; reaction to sign stimuli of, 47-49, 50; reproductive behavior of, 59-60
Blackbird, 66
Brood patch, 60, *69*, *70-71*
Brooding, of herring gull, *44-45*
Bullfinches, experiment with singing by, 98

Butterflies: courtship of, 36, 49; grayling, mating ritual of, 63-65

Camouflage, 111, 113-114
Canaries: nest-building pattern of, 59-60, *69*, *70-71;* singing experiment with bullfinches, 98
Cat, tuning out stimulus by, *46-47*
Caterpillars: advantage of communal living to, 111; eyed hawk moth, 50, *97;* and instinct to follow, *94;* position defense aid to, 119
Chaffinches, repeating normal song by, 98
Chicks: ability of to recognize shape, *98-99;* tests of vision of, *100-101*
Colonies, of gulls, 12, 111, *116-117*
Color blindness: and bees, 10, 35-36; and grayling butterflies, 40
Colors: ability of animals to recognize, 25-26; differences in, between bird sexes, 113-114; food stimulus to baby gull, *34*, 46-47, 50; recognition of, by bees, *11*, 35-36; recognition of, by grayling butterflies, 40-49; response to by insects, 23-25; as sign stimuli for stickleback, *40-41*, *42-43*
Community life: of army ants, 115; based on communications, 111-112; of bees, 110; of ducklings, 110; of penguins, *108-109;* in prairie dog town, *122-123;* prevalence of, 109-110; variety of, among black-headed gulls, *116-117*
Courtship: of black-headed gulls, *116-117;* of canaries, *70-71;* dance of ostrich, *72-73;* of grayling butterflies, 36, 63-65; of stickleback, *40-41*, *42-43;* of Tibetan barheaded geese, *54-55;* use of color in bird, 114
Crab, soldier, shelter of, *50-51*
Crop milk, 58
Crows, 7, 11-12, *116-117*, 119
Cuttlefish, 13-15, 121

Darwin, Charles, 8-9
Detectors, sensory, *26-27*, *28-29*, 32, 90
Diffuse light sense, 27
Division of labor: among bees, 110; among jewelfish, 110, *118*
Dogs, 19; conditioned by Pavlov's bell, 97; as followers of scent, 32
Dolphin, sound produced by, 31
Dragonfly, as food for toad, *102-103*
Drugs, effect on spiders, 56
Ducklings, social existence of, 110

Echo-location: by bats, 30-31, *74*, *76-77;* by whales, 31-32
Eels, migrations of, 76
Eggs: hatching of, by king penguins, *108-109;* laying of, by canaries, *70-71;* of paper wasps, *120-121;* reaction of gulls to, *44-45*, *104-105;* retrieval of lost, by birds, *78-79;* simultaneous laying of, by

gulls, 12; ventilation of, by stickleback, 9-10, *42-43*
Environment, 19; as behavior control, 57-60
Estrogen, 60
Evolution: of animal behavior, 119-124; compromises in, 119-121; man's place in, 124; preservation of the fit in, 97, 119; theory of, 8
Eyes: compound, *18*, *21*, 27-28; effect of on orientation, 85-88; human, *21;* insect, *21*, 27-28; octopus, *21*, *22;* of spider, *33;* of vertebrates, 27; of water beetle, 41

Fabre, J. Henri, *9*
Falcon, sharp vision of, 28
Fish: hearing in, 20-23; orientation in, 87
Flies, 57; method of tasting by, *26-27;* optomotor response displayed by, 85-86
Food: of prairie dogs, 123; self-produced by paper wasps, 121; tastes learned by experience, *102-103;* of water beetle, 41
Foxes, 12-13, *116-117*, 124
Frisch, Karl von, *10-11*, 20-23, 25, 35-36
Frog, tickling experiment with, 101-102

Geese: compromise shape of feet of, 119-121; division of labor among, 110; graylag, communication postures of, *112-113;* graylag, diving maneuver of, *89;* imprinting behavior on young, 96, 103; snow, *17;* threat postures in, 71; Tibetan barheaded, mating ritual of, *54-55*
Grasshopper, attracting of, *24-25*
Gravity, orientation of fish to, 82-84, 87
Great tit (bird), *107*
Gulls, 8, 67, 76, 121; advantages of communal living to, 111; black-headed, changed breeding places of, 121-124; black-headed, community existence of, *116-117;* black-headed, defensive habits of, 11-12; black-headed, imperfect defenses of, 119; black-headed, innate response of young, 96; herring, *34*, *44-45*, 46-47, 50; learning process of young, 95-97; recognition of their eggs by, *44-45*, *104*

Hairs: directional guides on praying mantis, 90; lateral lines on fish, 32; orientation guides on fish, 82-84; as sensory aids on insects, 29; sensory detectors of water bugs, *28-29;* sensory organs of flies, *26-27*
Harlow, Harry F., *48*, 99
Hawks, shape of, source of fear, *98-99*
Hearing: in bats, 30-31; in fishes, 20-23; as guide in orientation, 82; in insects, 30; in whales, 31-32
Hen, as mother to kittens, *52-53*
Hess, Carl von, 35
Holst, Erich von, 85

Hormones, 57-60, 69, 70-71
Horsefly, eye of, *18*
Housefly, *26-27*
Hunting habits: of cuttlefish, 13-15, 121; of digger wasp, 61, *62-63*

Imprinting: of behavior, 96; timing of, important, 103
Instinct, an inborn trait, 94-106

Jewelfish, 110; schooling of young, *118*

Kittens, *52-53;* caution of, *92*

Language: animal, 17, 71, 111-114; of bats, 30-31, *74;* postures of graylag geese as, *112-113;* of whales, 31
Lateral lines, sense organs of fish, 32
Learning: by toad, *102-103;* dependence of, on timing, 103; variance of, among animals, 103-105
Light: as controller of sex glands, 58, 59; detection of infrared, 26, *30;* reactions of bees to, 35-36; reactions to colors of, 23-26
Lorenz, Konrad Z., *17*

Man: behavior a result of experience, 99, 106; programmed behavior, 106; lessons to learn from animal behavior, 114-118
Mittelstaedt, Horst, 85
Monkeys: maternal relationship affects adult behavior of, 99, 106; rhesus, reaction of to "mothers," *48-49,* 99; source for human behavior studies, 106
Moth, yucca, 9
Motherly care, need of, 99, 106
"Mothers," monkey reaction to fake, *48-49*
Murres (birds), 104-105
Muscular activity, and animal behavior, 15
Myna bird, ability to imitate, 98

Natural selection, 8; evolution by, 97, 119
Negative feedback, 66, 72, 82
Nerve cells, 57, 72
Nervous system, 15-16, 82, 85
Nest building: behavior patterns in, by birds, 60, 70, *71;* by canaries, 59-60; by stickleback, 9-10, 41, *42-43,* 57

Octopus, 13; recognition of shape by, *22*
Optomotor response, 85-86
Orientation, 75-90; by bats, *74,* 76-77; by bears, 83; by bees, 88; of birds, 75-76; in fish, 76, 78, 82-84, *87;* of geese, *89;* migratory, of starlings, 88; mutual, by antelope, *85;* of rats, *90-91*
Ostrich, courtship dance of, *72-73*
Ovipositor, 9

Pavlov, Ivan, *9,* 97
Pecking ability, in chicks, *100-101*
Penguins, king, community life of, *108-109*
Pigeons, feeding of young by, 58
Pike (fish), 78
Pit vipers (snake), 26
Pituitary gland, 57, 58, 59
Prairie dogs, community of, 2, *122-123*
Praying mantis, 78, 90
Programming, of responses, 96-97, 99-102
Prolactin, 58
Protective devices: burrow of soldier crab, *50-51;* companionship, 32; eyespots of moth, 47-49; fighting stance of baboon, *64-65;* schooling of jewelfish, *118*

Rats: ability to reason, 104-105; feeding experiments with, 68; testing of, in mazes, *90-91;* training of, to get food, 14-15, 104-105
Rattlesnakes: diamond-back, *123;* detection of infrared light by, 26, *30;* response to heat by, *26-27, 30*
Reason, inborn, in rats, *104-105*
Reflex, conditioned, 9, *34*

Salmon, spawning migration of, 76, 88
Schneirla, Theodore C., *11*
Security, need of by rhesus monkeys, *48-49,* 99, 106
Sense organs: as guides in orientation, 79-90; hairs as, *26-27, 28-29;* how they work, 19-32; lateral lines, 32; need for, 19; and nervous system, 15-16; in rattlesnakes, 26-27; tactile, 29; use of, for communication, 112-114
Sense receptors, 57, 79-82
Sex glands, 57, 58, 70
Shape: as mating stimulus for stickleback, *42-43;* recognition of, 28-29, 38, 51-52, 78-79, *98-99;* stimulus of, to herring gulls *44-45,* 50
Shrimp, as prey of cuttlefish, 13-15, 121
Sight: of bees in ultraviolet light, 20, *31;* of digger wasp in hunting, 61-*62;* of falcon, 28; reflex, of baby birds, *36-37*
Signals: need of, for stickleback spawning, 113; nerve, 82-84; response to, *34,* 40-41, 114; through sense organs, 112-114; sounds as, 113; visual, 113-114; warning, by antelope, 85
Size: reaction to, of young thrushes, 51-52; as stimulus to butterflies, 38, 49; stimulus of, to gulls, 44-45, *49-50*
Skinner, B. Frederick, *14*
Smell: in butterfly courtship, 63-65; as chemical sense, 32, 112; communication signal by barnacles, 112; as guide in orientation, 82; in hunting food, 41-44, 61-*62;* poor in birds, 19-20
Sonar, 30-32, *74, 76-77,* 80-81
Sound: attraction to grasshoppers, *24-25;*

as signals, *113*
Spiders: effect of drugs on, *56;* imperial, *61;* wolf, *33*
Squirrels, nut cracking by, 102-103
Starlings, *67;* internal clock of, 88
Sticklebacks, 9-10, 57; mating colors of, *40-41, 42-43;* need signal to spawn, 113
Stimuli, 19-20, 23, 37, 52; as behavior controls, 58-63, 88; chemical, as mating signal, 37, 63-65; color as, 25-26, *34,* 38, *40-41, 42-43,* 46-47, 50; conditioned response to, 97; contrast, 50; of hairs in fish orientation, 82-84; hormones as, 57-60, 69, 70-71; human reactions to, 106; maternal, by hen, *52-53;* misfiring of, 47-49, 52; multiple, at same time, 68-71; nerve cells as, 57; reactions to, 52, 55, 70-71, 88; of shape and size, 37-38, *42-43, 44-45,* 49-52; sign, *38-39, 40-41,* 46-52; of smell, 41-44, 61-*62;* as stopping signals, 65-71; supernormal stimulation, 44-45, 49-50; tactile, 29; tuning out of, 44, *46-47*
Sun: orientation of fish to, 87; orientation of migrating starlings to, 88

Target value, 84, 85, 86-88
Taste: as chemical sense, 32; organs of, in flies, *26-27*
Thrushes, reactions by young, 51-52
Toad, eating habits learned by, *102-103*
Touch: as behavior stimulus, *34,* 58, 60, 62, *63;* sense of, in spider, 32; as stickleback's spawning signal, 113

Ultrasonic sound: by bats, 30-31, *74,* 76-77; by whales, 31, 80-81
Ultraviolet light, reaction of bees to, 20, *31*

Vision: aided by sensory hairs, 90; and color sensitivity, 23-26; extent of, in animals, 27-28; as guide in orientation, 82; and orientation of geese, *89;* and recognition of shape, 28-29, 78-79, 84, *98-99;* in relation to target value, 85-88; stimuli of, in butterflies, 36-40; tests of, in chicks, *100-101;* of water beetle, 41, 44

Warmth: mother stimulus of, *48-49;* need of, by birds, 119
Wasps: digger, hunting pattern of female, 61, *62-63;* digger, recognition of shape by, 28-29, 78-79, 84, 88; paper, community life of, *120-121*
Water insects, *28-29*
Water strider, *28*
Whales: beluga, 31; humpback, *80-81;* reason for strandings of, 31-32; use of sonar by, 31-32, *80-81*
Wisconsin, University of, experiments with monkeys at, *48-49,* 99

Yucca moth, 9

Credits

The sources for the illustrations that appear in this book are shown below. Credits for the pictures from left to right are separated by commas, from top to bottom by dashes.

For Further Reading

Berrill, Jacquelyne, *Wonders of the Wild*. Dodd, 1955
Burton, Maurice, *Curiosities of Animal Life*. Sterling, 1959
Cooper, Elizabeth K., *Insects and Plants; the amazing partnership*. Harcourt, Brace and World, 1963
Cosgrove, Margaret, *The Strange World of Animal Senses*. Dodd, 1961
Darling, Louis, *The Gull's Way*. Morrow, 1965
Penguins. Morrow, 1956
Dudley, Ruth H., *Partners In Nature*. Funk and Wagnalls, 1965
Gilbert, Bil, *How Animals Communicate*. Pantheon Books, 1966
Hyde, Margaret O., *Animal Clocks and Compasses; from animal migration to space travel*. McGraw-Hill, 1960
Mason, George F., *Animal Appetites*. Morrow, 1966
Animal Clothing. Morrow, 1955
Animal Sounds. Morrow, 1948
Animal Tails. Morrow, 1958
Animal Tools. Morrow, 1951
Animal Weapons. Morrow, 1949
Selsam, Millicent E., *How Animals Tell Time*. Morrow, 1967
The Language of Animals. Morrow, 1962
Simon, Hilda, *Exploring the World of Social Insects*. Vanguard Press, 1962
Storer, John Humphreys, *The Web of Life*. Devin-Adair, 1953
Sutton, Ann, *Animals On the Move*. Rand McNally, 1965
Tinbergen, Niko, *Curious Naturalists*. Basic Books, 1959
Ubell, Earl, *The World of the Living*. Atheneum, 1965
Vevers, Gwynne, *Animals of the Arctic*. McGraw-Hill, 1964
Weyl, Peter, *Men, Ants and Elephants*. Viking, 1959
Wiley, James (ed.), *Beasts, Brains and Behavior*. Four Winds, 1965

Acknowledgments

The editors are indebted to Dr. Kenneth D. Roeder, Professor of Physiology, Department of Biology, Tufts University, Medford, Massachusetts, who read and commented on the entire text. The editors are also indebted to the staff of the LIFE Nature Library edition of *Animal Behavior*, from which this volume has been adapted. The staff for this edition was Stanley Fillmore, editor; Eric Gluckman, designer; John von Hartz, writer; Eleanor Feltser, Susan Marcus, Theo Pascal, researchers; David L. Harrison, copyreader; Gloria Cernosia, art assistant.